Lovely She Goes!

A Story of Arctic Trawling

by

William Mitford

J. B. LIPPINCOTT COMPANY

Philadelphia and New York

1970

ACKNOWLEDGEMENTS

I wish to record my indebtedness to Captain C. H. Ives of Grimsby who accepted with smiling fortitude the demands I made upon his time and bore with tolerance the months I spent under his command.

His comments have been invaluable and while I accept full responsibility for the facts and opinions expressed in this book I hope he will consider the result worthy of his patience. Whatever small merit this book may have is offered to him in token repayment.

I gratefully acknowledge the courtesy extended to me by the operational director of trawlers, Dennis A. Roberts, and that of the ship's husband Ken West, for whose practical help I have long been grateful. To Pete McKillop, and the staff of the crews signing on office I offer thanks for many a remembered kindness and gesture of goodwill. I owe a lasting debt to my fellow trawlermen, not least for their companionship. I avail myself of the opportunity to thank the countless individuals who showed interest and gave advice, and those who offered hospitality. Where these have been declined I accept the loss as mine and hope the offers may one day be renewed.

I thank Captain A. J. Denison – whose sharp eye and daunting presence should have turned me into a more efficient trawlerman – for his forbearance when my performance was less than consistently admirable. I include Mates Ken Micklin and Jeff Peterson; Bosuns Jim Flaherty and Barry Almond. These four above others convinced me that the sea is one of the few callings left in a standardised world where individuals matter.

To the only heroine in this book – *Arctic Fox* – I give affectionate recognition.

INTRODUCTION

A trawler left Grimsby at midnight on the 3rd January on the first of the fourteen trips she was expected to make that year. Six miles down the Humber she turned under a full helm and struck north for five-and-a-half days. Her speed was $13\frac{1}{2}$ knots.

She was no bigger than a corvette, and the smallest vessel of her class to go deep sea voyaging within the Arctic Circle. Where she went – and how far – was left to the judgement of her captain.

Three weeks later she returned with 126 tons of fish, having covered 3,421 miles across two oceans.

The first of these oceans was the Atlantic; the second was the Arctic. She was to survive them both.

She penetrated the northern ice fields and passed beyond the ice barrier of the Arctic Seas to reach the southern limits of the Polar Cap in winter.

How she did this – and why – is told in the pages of this book.

She's a real ship; only her name has been changed. The men are real – all twenty of them. They didn't talk much, and when they did it seldom revealed what was uppermost in their minds. Often they talked of things that mattered least of all. Trawlermen are like that.

This true story has been compressed in time and event into a single journey for the purpose of the narrative. Perhaps it will explain men's savage love and contempt for it all. Perhaps it will reveal something else besides. It will show what the sea can do to a man, and what he can do against its tireless malice. The narrative is disjointed because it happened that way. Passionate because this elegant little ship didn't die after all. Beautiful, violent and funny because it was all of those things.

CHAPTER ONE

'Let go the headrope – let go aft – half astern – starboard thirty.'

Arctic Fox backed away from North Wall. Leaving her berthing position she met the 8-knot tide and turned into the tideway still going astern. She eased in, losing sternway as her bows drew a lazy arc across the water. 'Stop engines – helm amidships – port twenty – slow ahead.'

At 'Slow Ahead' she gathered speed, carrying the tide with her. Grimsby looked lonely and remote, as if the ship and its crew hardly had anything to do with it. *Arctic Fox's* deck lights came on, showing a patina of frost covering the life-boats and the Red Ensign flying at the jackstaff, its frayed edges licking the wind. From the whaleback, a command centuries old: 'Haul taut – and belay the headrope.' With the ship square to the lock came the cry which committed her to the open sea: 'LOVELY SHE GOES!'

The ship gathered speed. The sea came off the bow lightly edged like a gull's feather. Men's scalps crinkled, and the wind lifted their hair. On either side the land was just visible, the shores fretted by the surf. Spurn Lighthouse, embedded in foam, passed astern. It was no longer possible to see the foreshortened figures standing at the lock gates, but they would still be there. Shore lights winked and an Aldis flashed a signal. A line of well-dressed gulls banked away on the air currents and turned for the shore. Grimsby had gone. Eyes turned towards the sea, staring with grim faces at the thin grey line where the ocean met the sky. It was easier now they were committed. It was easier to throw off the infection of the land and stare at the torn ribbons of cloud before going below to the fo'c's'le. It was Wednesday, early morning, January 1967.

This brutal voyage began just like all the others. There was no foreboding as the Humber reached high water. From a house in Park Street Harry had packed his own shirt-bag and caught a bus to Humber Street. In nearby Rutland Street Wacker waved goodbye to his mother without looking back. At the house on the corner of Heneage Road Paddy warmly embraced the blonde with a glass in her hand. She didn't resist, but she was glad to see him go. 'Buster', looking the epitome of a homespun fisherman and smelling of rum, stopped a taxi in Victoria Street and climbed in with difficulty.

Only a few people had seen the ship leave. The old men in long overcoats who began every sentence 'I remember the time . . .' – they'd gone. The nightwatchman had gone – the one whose right hand fell open as you passed. The ship's husband was still there, ticking off the crew like he was founding a dynasty. The gulls – of course – cadging a lift down the Humber. The plonkies were there, muttering 'Five bob'll see me right', as they watched the tide tugging hard at the stern. The runner was still stalking the dock, wiping rain off the crew list and shouting 'Nine to come!' like a man announcing the plague. Several anonymous performers, some carrying things, some not, hung around like they always did. A girl wearing clogs spat into a puddle. A mongrel barked at *Arctic Fox's* Mate – and looked surprised at the cheers.

It was such an ordinary beginning, but it happened so often it was bound to be ordinary . . . .

By breakfast time on Wednesday the weather began to freshen from the east, filling the nostrils with oil fumes and the odour of fish. Along the ship's rail a solemn jury of gulls turned head to wind. Ahead lay the North Sea – grey, unsmiling and strangely calm. Beyond, far beyond, lay two oceans; ferocious in winter, treacherous at all times. One was the Atlantic, a thousand fathoms deep – the graveyard of 3,012 ships and more than 30,000 men from a bitter war. The other was the Arctic – often beautiful and often deadly. Both oceans were neutral. They froze men to iron or gave them hope without rescue. Sometimes they simply let them go.

Trawlers have died in these oceans, mostly because the ice built up faster than exhausted men could chop it away, sometimes because the men themselves were unlucky, resigned or just not tough enough. There will always be others to take their place.

8

The sea entices that kind of man. If the Atlantic and the Arctic were neither remote nor neutral men would not voyage across the North Sea to challenge them. Twenty men in a small, efficient ship would be safe in harbour. Twenty men. Quarrelling, lusting, falling into debt.

It was starting to rain. It grew a little colder as darkness fell at the end of the first day at sea.

CHAPTER TWO

The ship: Cochrane's built her at Selby in 1960, as a rakish, graceful tribute to a long tradition. At least that's how she looked the first time one saw her. Amos and Smith built her engines with the care associated with their name. Oil firing replaced coal some time later and she'd been in commission ever since. From the higher mysteries of the bridge to the rat-free bilges, everyone had done their famous best and nearly everyone had succeeded. Where they'd failed almost anyone would have failed, but later will do for that . . .

Arctic Fox displaced a thousand tons and measured 200 ft. overall. As an ocean-going vessel she was a good 'sea ship', with a top speed of 13.6 knots. The Navy, with its fondness for calculated austerity, would have considered her bridge to be grossly self-indulgent with its armchair, radiators and deep blue carpet. It was even panelled in dark wood, and had that faint air of intimidation common to most ships, even colliers and tramps. Equipment included two Radars, radio transmitter and receiver, ship-to-shore telephones, depth sounders and two echometers. There was also a marine log which recorded the distance covered at sea and was sensitive enough to record speeds as low as one knot. In addition there was a meter for measuring the direction and speed of water currents. The brass ashtrays, window catches and telegraph pedestals all gleamed brightly and tended to confirm the general air of efficiency. The bridge windows facing

9

for'ard gave an unrestricted view of the foredeck – the main place of work during fishing operations. The deck planks were teak, caulked with oakum and pitch, and scoured at the end of each trip with chloride of lime and scrubbed with deck brushes till white.

She behaved well under helm and held a straight course when it suited her. She had a considerable depth of hull for fish stowage, and the fuel needed for long voyages, but there were only five watertight bulkheads below the waterline and the hull comprised plates of single thickness. She had one blemish which sharp eyes couldn't fail to notice. *Arctic Fox* had come from dry dock, fresh from the revenging hands of the dockyard-mateys. Her tough, elegant bows had red lead around the fresh rivet scars, mostly below the waterline. The spare trawl doors had been secured to the port rail and would have to be keel hauled before they could be used on the towing side. The winch platform had been raised a mere six inches – enough to upset familiar and customary movement (difficult enough in thigh boots). The net bins looked like someone's idea of private Hell, and odd bits of welding had turned the fore-deck into a miniature obstacle course. Every imaginable spare part that could have belonged to another ship had been dumped under *Arctic Fox's* whaleback, and some comedian had treated the lavatory seat to a coat of slow-drying orange paint. A large box labelled 'Explosive Signal Rockets – Please Dump in Deep Water' was found buried under 61 empty beer cans (the Bosun counted them), and a parted heaving line – big enough for the new Queen Elizabeth – lay on the bathroom floor.

Nothing had survived the docking period unscathed. The winch brakes had been left to rust with what appeared to be conscientious determination, and the coal on the boat-deck and elsewhere was enough for twice round the world. In comparison, the freshwater tank in the forepeak was bone dry, and the new pound boards were all six inches too long.

Arctic Fox inspired confidence more than sentiment. There was this immense air of purpose which nothing could quench. The wide-awake look that passed unnoticed until she drew along-

side another trawler. Attractive, too. With her trim black upper-
works, freshly painted forepeak leading to the raised and
cambered fo'c's'le head, bright green tarpaulins covering the
anchor windlass – she looked worth every penny of the £198,000
it cost to build her.

CHAPTER THREE

The crew: The Skipper was twenty-nine and stood five feet four.
A wiry, muscular frame and strong arms tapered into long, slender
hands and fingers which in conversation often appeared not to
belong to him. Ambitious. Vigorous and fatalistic, with an abrupt
manner which revealed a power-house of energy and stamina.
A vulnerable man – the sort that stirred compassion in women
and doubt in men. That side of his personality open to scrutiny
showed a zestful confidence punched home with conviction. Only
his eyes gave him away, and then only when he was tired, or
trusted you. Although he never went down on to the deck
he had none of the mystery of remoteness. He wore no uniform,
uttered the same expletives as his men, was no better educated
than they were and shared the same proletarian background. For
five years he was a mate, and an excellent one, so he knew his
deckies' attitude towards authority – and authority was all he had.
The men addressed him as 'Skipper' and usually waited to be
spoken to first. Except the Badger, who hollered at him in an
uncringing, man-to-man tone and called him 'Boss'. His reputation with the crew rested entirely on his ability to find fish and
as there were alternative courses open to him and only he could
make the decisions, he was often racked with doubt and mindful
of the naked power of the 'Gaffers' who could beach him any
time they wished.

In contrast to the spirit, the flame with its odd intensity, there
was silence and restraint. Sometimes he would appear and impose
silence on the bridge without any attempt whatsoever. His re-

moteness, his orders given in a conversational tone with no particular expression in his voice, influenced the slightest movement of those around him. His strange economy of movement, so tellingly effective when things needed doing quickly, made men feel they were somehow at fault, too slow off the mark, lazy even. There was never any feeling of shared responsibility when the Captain was present on the bridge. Men waited to be told instead of acting for themselves – as they were capable of doing. Whether it was instinctive or merely chosen habit he encouraged the feeling that it was his job to command and he wanted to do it alone.

All ten deckhands slept for'ard, whilst the remaining nine crew members slept aft, each with his own cabin. The most senior of these was the Chief Engineer. 'Chiefy' was a Warwickshire man and had the Warwickshire look – wary, ironic, and consciously disbelieving. He was also extremely thrifty. His one-piece (and only) boiler suit was so encrusted with grease that it stood up on its own when Chiefy took it off, and his woollen 'hat' was, in fact, a tea cosy embroidered with daisies. During his rare visits to the outside of the ship he pulled this tea cosy down around his face leaving only his nose showing through the spout hole, and one ear sticking out of the opening made for the tea-pot handle. The boots he wore during the twelve hours spent on watch were handed over to his Second before Chiefy went watch below. The Second wore them for a further twelve hours and then handed them back to his Chief. Being in use for 168 hours a week the boots never lasted out the six months' guarantee given by the makers so Chiefy sent them back and demanded a new pair. Apart from the initial purchase he had not bought a new pair for more than three years. In addition he had the finest collection of pornographic tattoos – extending from the navel to the buttocks – of anyone sailing out of G.Y. It cost ten cigarettes to view them. The Chief seldom came on to the bridge and when he did so it was either to collect his rum ration or report some fault with the engines and leave immediately. Likewise the Skipper had no authority to enter the engine room and would not do so unless invited. The Chief thought of the engine room as a detached unit, sufficient, self-reliant. Outsiders (meaning deckhands) were suffered, sometimes tolerated, seldom welcomed.

He reacted violently to such remarks as, 'Don't you *ever* take your vest off?' and practically charged money if anyone borrowed a spanner.

The Chief and his three engineers each worked an 84-hour week made up of two six-hour watches each day. Their work consisted of regulating the flow of oil to the burners, putting grease and oil on moving parts and paying constant attention to the engine room telegraph so as to be able to obey instantly any command given by the bridge.

Chiefy was a good engineer with a genuine love of machinery but was less concerned than he should have been with matters outside the engine room.

The 'down below' men were all trades union supporters, and both firemen were Deenies who saved their rum in medicine bottles and washed themselves every day.

The Sparks played little part in the lives of the deckmen. Being classed as an officer he ate his meals in the cabin and visited the mess-deck to gather information and display his natural superiority The deckies addressed him as 'Commander' to which appellation he airily conceded. As he had no authority over anyone aboard he emphasized his primacy in other ways. In his berth he displayed a uniform jacket of an officer of the Merchant Navy, emblazoned with campaign ribbons from a war he could only have read about. During fishing operations he seldom left the radio room.

The cook was English by birth and could claim to be a Lincolnshire man because he'd never lived anywhere else, but his physical characteristics showed a mixed ancestry. He had slanting eyes and thick, sensuous lips set in a round, flat face. In some moods he possessed a particularly villainous aspect to which the dark pigmentation of his skin and other negroid traces gave emphasis. He was known as 'Liquorice All Sorts' to everyone except

Buster, who was never one to subscribe to other people's humour and always addressed the cook as 'Chef'. The cook was popular inasmuch as he was good at his job. He cooked three large and widely varied meals each day for twenty-one days on a coal-fired stove in a small galley. In addition, he baked his own bread. Below the burn scars on his left forearm were a number of tattoos, one of which read 'Death before Employment'. A pronouncement which was in no way indicative of the cook's true nature. Even in rough weather he maintained a foothold in the galley by clinging with both hands to the cold water pipe over his head and swinging to and fro with the motion of the ship – a posture which drew the inevitable remarks about his antecedents and the usual offer of bananas. During severe weather he still refused to give up his galley and sang and cursed alternately as the motion of the ship sent boiling food and saucepans flying about and the tiny galley became a pandemonium of crashing china and utensils, with 'Liquorice All Sorts' swinging above the lot swearing loudly.

Among those who slept aft was the Mate. The Mate was a tough professional with a weakness for rum. His face, like all good faces, was interesting to look at and lasted in the memory. His brown eyes seldom revealed anything but bleak amusement, and a suspicion of human motives came easily to him. His compact, agile body supported thick, muscular arms tapering into short, hard, capable fingers. The ice burns on his palms showed he often worked without gloves. His predictably abrupt manner concealed a shyness few suspected except his wife – the best-looking woman in Grimsby. He couldn't hope to be liked, and was sensible enough not to try.

He was obeyed because of his authority which was maintained by physical distance when not on duty or at mealtimes when he ate with the Skipper and Chief Engineer in the officers' cabin. He was respected because he did a potentially dangerous and always gruelling job on the open deck alongside the deckmen and shared the bleakness of their lives on other occasions. He had no special relationship with his Skipper, and like many mates

14

ate his food in silence when his Captain was present at meal-times. The Mate's general air of conviction and determination was perfectly genuine and complemented his authority in a way which gave an appearance of ease and perfection to his quick and accurately timed movements on the deck. Amongst men who greatly admired physical strength he gave an example others would follow beyond the limits of their endurance, and by so doing made what was probably his greatest single contribution to the efficiency of *Arctic Fox's* experienced crew. A contribution which was seen and understood by his relatively inexperienced Skipper, who was to use it – and use it deliberately in the days that followed – to drive his ship and his men to extremes of danger under circumstances he could not have exploited without the knowledge that his Mate carried the crew with him.

The Bosun was another of those quartered aft, and had a single berth next to the Mate's. The Bosun was more widely read than most of the crew and was aware of things just beyond his reach. His capacity to feel and to respond was greater than that of most fishermen, and both heightened and intensified his ability to absorb knowledge. He was poorly educated and left school at 14 because of poverty at home. At $14\frac{1}{2}$ he was driving a horse-drawn fish cart on the Docks. At 16 he went to sea as a deckie learner and had been at sea ever since. His speech was poor, and in his youth had rendered him almost inarticulate. After a difficult personal struggle he had won the battle to express himself, but remained poignantly aware of the direction his life had taken.

The Bosun was a fine trawlerman, knowledgeable and experienced. The moment a ship was hull up on the horizon he could tell you her name, who her skipper was, what her mate was like and name those members of *Arctic Fox's* crew who had sailed in her at one time or another. He would know whether or not she had been lengthened since she was built and how she reacted to rough weather. Like the rest of *Arctic Fox's* crew, he was free of sentiment as regards his ship and had no attachment or loyalty to any one trawler even after having sailed in her for a year or more. Neither did he believe there was any glamour in being a fisherman. Dressed in the usual 'Fear Naught' trousers and speckled jersey, with a red and white polka-dot muffler round his neck, one would have picked him out anywhere as a fisherman.

Buster should have slept for'ard in the cramped fo'c's'le, but for some reason which no one really understood he always had a berth to himself mid-ships. Someone said it was because that particular berth was the only one with a plug suitable for Buster's electric razor. On previous trips the Mate had ordered him back to the fo'c's'le, but later he was found to have dragged his mattress and lavender sheets along mid-ships and quietly settled back into his more exclusive quarters. There is no doubt he needed more space than the other deckmen. His 21 tins of steak and kidney pudding, toilet rolls and 14 lb. tins of biscuits took up a lot of room. And his radio and coffee percolator both needed plug points not available in the crew's quarters. He also had a lot of sea gear which he hung out to dry along the rail beside the engine room cat-walk. When the engineers complained of the sea water dripping down on them he moved everything to the galley – until the cook complained and he moved it back to the cat-walk again. Everyone spoke of Buster as the biggest liar who ever sailed out of G.Y. He had the gift of spinning a good yarn and making it suspect – even when it was known to be true! His witnesses, when he bothered to offer any, were always drawn from the ranks of those absent or strangers whose names he didn't quite catch at the time. He spoke gravely of the dark days of the war when he trawled up magnetic mines from the bed of the Humber, with the Royal Navy hove to at a safe distance watching him. He talked of the time he shot down two Dorniers during one afternoon, alone on the boat-deck with the skipper dying on the bridge and the mate cowering in the scuppers wearing a life-belt. No one could actually imagine Buster in this role – instead they thought of him as the one most likely to be found with his lifebelt in the scuppers – but they were obliged to accept these stories in silence because he was the only one aboard old enough to have been in the war at all and as in most of the stories his

16

companions unfortunately died there were no witnesses. Although no one (except the galley boy) believed anything he said he seldom lost his audience. His success might have been due to his lack of shame, which shone with the kind of simplicity sometimes mistaken for innocence. His other pastime was poker. Most of the crew agreed that to play poker with Buster was to invite bankruptcy, but time can drag at sea – particularly when steaming up to the fishing ground.

The galley boy was 16. Between bouts of sea-sickness he peeled vegetables, laid the mess-deck table, washed up after meals and read comics in his berth opposite the galley. He was for ever throwing refuse away over the weather side of the ship – against the wind – and spent much of his spare time washing custard out of his hair, pulling egg shells out from under his string vest and scraping tapioca from inside his rubber boots. Apart from an endless capacity for sleep and his inability to distinguish between the lee and the weather side of the ship he was always forgetting things or losing them altogether. During one trip he lost five tin openers, sixteen pots and a sack of cabbages weighing half a hundredweight. He absent-mindedly threw the mincer over the side, and used five gallons of foam to put out a fire in a matchbox. It was generally agreed that he cost the 'Gaffers' more in lost property than he earned in wages. On one occasion he was asked to supply vinegar for the mess-deck table – and supplied instead the cook's rum which All Sorts saved in a vinegar bottle kept in the pantry. Before the mistake was noticed the rum had disappeared – most of it inside the Badger, who was most unhelpful when answering the cook's questions later on. He was generally accepted by the crew and was noticeably friendly with Buster who was teaching him how to play poker.

Of the most flamboyant character aboard mention has already been made. The sobriquet, spontaneously generated and later consecrated by use until 'Bob' dropped from the vocabulary and 'The Badger' emerged, had unusual origins. Clothing bought from a shop had to be enlarged before he could wear it. His mother,

17

a woman with a number of original ideas, made the alterations herself. Bob's mother made trawl nets at home for a large firm in G.Y. and kept a jackdaw trained to fly to and from the off-licence (and later the betting shop) with the day's orders. During her spare time she made large gussets from white sail-cloth which she machined into the seat of Bob's jeans and coats. Thus enlarged, these garments clothed, however inadequately, her son's 21-stone bulk. Rigged out in this fashion, any other man could expect a certain amount of genial ridicule, but his stripes troubled no one as much as they troubled the neighbourhood's dogs. Bob had always been troubled by dogs. Now they snatched at his trousers and barked at his heels wherever he went. They'd even started waiting for him outside his house in the morning. Lumbering along with the pack behind him, he gave every appearance of a large badger harried by dogs. Someone noticed the analogy and the sobriquet had arrived. When greeting someone he knew he lumbered straight at him with his head set forward and his massive shoulders moving from side to side. He took no notice of people he had never seen before and drank neat rum straight from the bottle without noticeable effect. Girls were fascinated by him and most were terrified as well. To be hugged by the Badger must have been quite an experience.

The sea had claimed him as it had claimed many others – by custom and the availability of suitable employment. Despite his roistering he never missed a trip. Open-handed, affectionate, genial and completely unscrupulous, he had a practical sagacity marred only by a lack of thrift. He had no cerebral occupation other than reading comics and picking winners, and these were secondary when it came to giving parties. As a trawlerman the Badger's skill and experience were both outstanding, but he used neither to the full unless he had to. Work for work's sake was not his strong suit. During steaming up he did little in the way of work and steaming back he did less – which in his case meant nothing at all. Under extreme provocation one could discern out-bursts of energy and ostensible movements of arms and legs, but in reality they amounted to very little. Shackles would be picked up and banged down, followed by a quite arbitrary pulling of ropes and lifting of pound boards – which fell back into the positions they previously occupied as soon as the eye of authority drifted elsewhere. It was during fishing operations that he really came into his own. His great physique, allied to an iron will, made him a completely reliable crew member. Gales, hurricane winds, mountainous seas, were merely incentives to greater effort, and his speed in moments of danger amazed everyone. Once, when the net dragged him over the side and into the sea, he survived by clinging to the mesh, using his free hand to pull the boots off his would-be rescuer who almost drowned in his attempt to save the Badger. With the aid of a boat hook lowered from the deck he pulled himself inboard with one hand, gripping his rescuer with the other. Later he replaced the man's boots with a new pair. (The outfitter, thinking they were for the Badger, supplied size 12 and the man needed four pairs of boot stockings to prevent them falling off.)

It was on his first trip to sea that he met the Whippit. They had much in common – a sea-faring tradition at home and a thirst for danger at all times. They were, as the saying goes, 'made for each other' – and if the Devil ever contrived a more troublesome pair they have yet to appear in Grimsby. Drunken, licentious, irreverent, incapable of servility of any kind, these two took to the sea remarkably well. The 'Gaffers' tolerated them, too. For one thing they never missed a trip.

In the dialect of south-west Lincolnshire a Whippit is a nimble person of small stature given to mischief. The Whippit's mother (who had christened him Frederick) changed her mind before he was four years old and gave him the pseudonym which he has never ceased to justify. He was thrown off his first ship for being 'saucy' – and off his second for being 'a thorough pest'. Like the Badger, the Whippit could always turn in a brilliant performance on the deck. He would run clever hands along the manilla head rope and find a hidden fault where it was marled on to the wings and square. He could lace the selvedges of wing and bosom without a glance at what he was doing, mask sisal thread into a lint of perfectly matched diamonds and then bate away the meshes with his mind elsewhere. Holding a buster crammed with pickles and cheese he would lay a line of bights along a rope with rapidly made clove hitches, all spaced to a fraction of an inch. To watch him enlarge the bights of bolsh on the ground rope, hung with icicles, was an impressive experience. Given the stage to himself he was outstanding. Put him with the rest of the daymen and he would whiffle away hour after hour, helping the Badger do precisely nothing.

Ken, the Mate: 'With those two making up the six I can reckon on four workers and a couple of card-playing beer drinkers chatting about horses and women and waiting for the knocking-off whistle to blow – there's no bastard justice.'

The remainder of the twenty-man crew all came from Grimsby or the districts close at hand. All were below 25, powerfully built and less piratical in dress and manner than the others Colin was the only man apart from the Badger to wear a gold ear-ring. Rubber Nose had more tattoos per square inch than Bill, but none of them could match the flamboyance of those already mentioned.

CHAPTER FOUR

Routine: on the way to the fishing grounds four deckhands watch-keep on the bridge, steering the ship. Three watches are set, each man standing watch for eight hours in two lots of four.

Collision regulations must be understood and a look-out kept for other shipping, especially at night, in rough weather or poor visibility. And in particular in the busy North Sea lanes. Not all oil rigs appear on the charts, and these must be seen in time for avoiding action to be taken. Vessels towing a trawl and those fishing with lines must be given seaway, particularly as the signal indicating the direction of their outlying gear is not always displayed. Some vessels display anchor balls when they are not at anchor but underway. Lightships are occasionally off station.

Not all fishing vessels show the regulation masthead light, and others ignore the prescribed fog signals when fishing. There is danger, too, from the big ships who neither reduce speed nor change direction when crossing a ship's intended course, because such alteration would mean writing an entry in the log. In addition, there are signals, buoys, flags and lights to be read off and understood, or quietly ignored.

There's the boredom, of course. Hours spent trying not to watch the clock crawling round. There's the baleful merchant-man who winks at you. Timber ships with a bilious roll, and one or two rusty heaps of shit who shouldn't have been at sea at all. Russians are rare and wary, training their zoom lenses in search of your main armament as they pass fine on the bow. There's the Royal Navy who look at you in a rather special way – suspicious of insolence – and trawlers from Iceland who can't bring themselves to look at all. The North Sea's full of ships. The well-behaved and efficient. Unexplained liners with spacious decks dressed overall in gulls, but rarely people. There's bound to be a waggish merchantman who signals, 'You have been drinking again, I see' (and they were right as it happened) or in one case, 'May we borrow your prostitute?' Sometimes there's the cargo boat who drops dead on your doorstep from engine failure. He's certain to be a foreigner without a megaphone, somehow they always are. It was all just bearable if you were lazy or romantic, but still preferable to the howling wilderness to come.

But bridge watch can – and often does – revert to one's own personal comfort. The feel of warm, dry boot stockings; the tea that tastes better than expected; the warm feeling as the first snow clogs the navigation lights. Night watch is worst, particularly when the fog comes down. There's bound to be a scare, perhaps from one of those Hamburg/New York types who *won't* give you seaway because they're bigger than you and they know it. And there's certain to be the oil rig dead ahead which the look-out was sure you'd passed five minutes before. All this is boring when you've seen it so often.

There's a first time for everything at sea, but nothing ever happens when you're waiting to record it. Last trip there was the crippled ship, holed below the waterline in a collision. Her crew abandoned her as the engine room filled with water, and *Arctic Fox* turned under full helm to claim her prize and make everyone on board rich with the hovel money she would bring. Someone else reached her first, and now they'll be rich – very rich indeed. Last trip also, a trembling Sparks emerged from the R. T. room with the stunning news that *Arctic Fox's* sister ship had ploughed bows on into a trawler from Aberdeen – and added to the shocked silence by saying, 'No report of survivors, I'm afraid'. The ship and her crew were safe, but it was a nasty moment just the same.

There was to be no such drama for the bridge watch on this trip, and as one pair relieved another the occasion was marked only by the routine boredom of repeating the course, changing the charts and swapping books full of semi-naked females. Even they failed to charm in the end, which is rather a pity.

The remaining six deckhands were 'daymen' and worked on the deck during the journey to the fishing ground. New wires have to be stowed, bridles measured with a two-foot stick and coiled ready for use, bobbin wires are reeved, nets made up and a complete new trawl got ready. Both derricks are swung out, the washer with its shute fixed in position, and finally the pounds are made up, bag ropes put in position, beckets put near at hand, and needles for mending the trawl are left charged and ready for use – this being the deckhand learner's special responsibility.

From the vantage point of the bridge on this January morning the sun lay low in the eastern quadrant and lit the frayed edges of the cloud banks the colour of pale rose madder. Further to the west the clouds low on the horizon were shot through with yellow shafts of light, their summits glowing like summer apricots, overlaid with drifting mist from some distant shore.

Arctic Fox continued to cleave her way through the choppy waters of the North Sea, and during the late evening of her third day out of Grimsby she was in the Atlantic Ocean, riding a nor'westerly swell with ease and confidence at a speed of $12\frac{1}{4}$ knots.

Straight on a course to the roof of the world – and endless night.

CHAPTER FIVE

From the bridge the Skipper moved to the chart room and, drawing a key from his pocket, unlocked a nest of long, mahogany drawers with solid brass handles all brightly polished. From one of these drawers he pulled out three blue-backed sea charts, laid them on the chart table and lowered the angle-poise lamp until the rim of the shade was six inches above them. Next he took up a pencil and lifted his dividers from their box. As he closed the lid he glanced at the date inside – 1804. The name alongside the date was the same as his own. The charts before him were creased and covered with pencilled course alterations, new fastenings and hurried calculations, all except the bottom one which was new, its surface covered almost entirely by the sea. He placed this on top of the others, and after much hesitation pushed the other two on to the floor. The chart in front of him showed the tip of a long finger of land, its coastline broken by fjords, the sea thrusting deep into its valleys and covering the sharp points of its many submerged islands. Following this archipelago he drew a line 240 miles out from the coast of Norway till it was intercepted by another line printed on the map itself. Next, he drew a circle round one of the principal islands of the archipelago and drew a line away from it at an angle. Beside this line he wrote:

'Latitude 74 degrees 30′ North. Longitude 19 degrees 00′ East. Round voyage in nautical miles – 2,980.'

Bear Island.

The Skipper's choice of fishing ground had been significant. This was his sixth trip as captain of his own ship. His five previous trips had been failures – or nearly so. He had chosen

Bear Island at this time of year because he was a gambler – as his father had been and his grandfather before that. Fishing, they told him, was a game of chance compounded of luck and intuition. Neither could say which was the most important. But both had taught him a lot. He possessed many of their old charts and records of past catches, some going back to the days of fishing smacks: information which detailed certain fishing grounds where large catches had been made in areas free from 'fastenings'. Other charts indicated where to place a buoy and in which direction to trawl in order to stay in the same depth of water. None of this information mentioned Bear Island.

The Skipper lingered for some minutes over the chart in front of him, keeping the point of his pencil on the bearing and then taking it away with difficulty as if the pencil had some gravitational pull of its own. It seemed to symbolise the attitude of a man who had gambled with something he wanted to keep – gambled not to win, but to keep from losing. There was a chance – a real one – that if he failed to 'make a trip' this time he would not be given any more trawlers to command. The 'Gaffers' had hinted as much, and as a gesture had allowed him to choose his own fishing ground instead of sending him to the North Cape and telling him to work back eastwards along the north coast. The Skipper resented being sent to North Cape by the 'Gaffers' and had said as much. He believed the twelve-mile limit had been responsible for his past failures. The twelve-mile limit round Norway is measured not straight out from the coastline but from one headland to the next. On a coastline broken by deep fjords and indented throughout its entire length large areas of fishing remained inaccessible, including those grounds which could be fished when the weather was rough.

On the morning of the fourth day *Arctic Fox* struck north with no alteration to her course. She protested now and then, as a woman is bound to do, but mostly she gave a brazen display of 'seakindliness' – lifting her elegant forepeak to the sky until the spray flew back and made her paint glisten in the sun; dipping her bow until the foam caressed the rail, causing the Mollies to lift one orange leg in protest. The Mollies would leave her soon

24

and turn for home, but for a few more hours they would continue to stand on the bow rails looking solemnly out at the malignant ocean. Their outward bound ritual at an end, they would leave with an occasional backward glance and reappear in exactly the same place when the ship entered home waters in two weeks' time.

With the weather fining away, the steaming routine continued its smooth and regular pattern. The daymen started work at eight o'clock and quietly knocked off again before nine. They re-appeared at nine forty-five because one of the watch came on to the mess-deck and told them the old man was awake and about to appear on the bridge. Fortunately, his habits were predictable. He always slept for the same interval of time and woke just before the watch called him. Sitting on his seat locker he acknowledged his call with a small movement of one hand without looking up. When asked if he wanted a pot of tea he would turn away with-out speaking, as if he regarded the question as unnecessary or too trivial. 'Laughing Boy's about to leave his cage,' was the signal for his imminent appearance, followed by a flurry as litter was swept from the bridge and tea-pots taken back to the galley. In reply to 'Good morning, Skipper' he would invariably answer: 'Check your course' or 'How can you keep a proper look-out if you talk all the time?' Then he would study the Radar before lowering the bridge window to frown at the sea and sky. Sometimes he stood with both elbows resting against the log table and listened to the radio telephone. Like most introverts he missed nothing and liked his motives to remain hidden. Men saw through him, though, almost as well as he saw through them.

When Rubber Nose handed over the watch to the relieving pair he did it with an air of authority and seriousness which belied his indolent nature. The old man knew this and wondered if this performance could possibly be better than the last. The Badger, to whom he normally handed over, accepted the ship into his personal charge with genuine boredom, adding, to Rubber Nose's intense annoyance: 'Don't forget yer handbag afore you go, Sonny.'

After a brief nod in the Skipper's general direction, he would produce a can of beer from inside his shirt and start to open it. This was usually enough for the old man, who retired back into his 'cage'. As the course would remain the same for the rest of the watch, the Badger preferred to act as look-out. For an hour or so he would mark the starboard wing (the port wing didn't have a radiator) and chat gaily to his many visitors. Once or twice he would break off and call sharply to the helmsman, 'Watch that liner over there!' and having savoured the pleasure of autocracy, resume his conversation with, 'They tell me that lass in the Bun Shop's got the clap again'. When the last of the visitors had rattled and clanked his way down the bridge ladder with dozens of empty beer cans the Badger would offer to take the wheel. Before doing so someone would have to fetch him a pile of sandwiches and more beer. It was on the wheel that he gave his most splendid study in non-vigilance. Without the least interest, he let the spokes run off through his fingers and checked them only when the sun moved the shadow of the mast along the bulkhead to a point where it masked the Badger's comic. He then turned the wheel until the shadow moved away and continued reading. The Radar might not have been there – he never gave it a glance. The only thing likely to ruffle his unassailable good humour was a heavy wave upsetting the beer. Having finished his comic he thought it time to liven things up in other directions. 'Starboard look-out relieved, Boss!' he would bawl with unnecessary urgency in the direction of the Captain's cabin. 'Does him good to know he's got a couple of good lads on the bridge for a change. He likes a shout now and then – stops him bobbing off.' Once, when coming across a flashing red light low in the water he called out, 'Brothel dead ahead. Shall I come alongside, Boss?' His best remembered 'gaff' happened the day he closed with a smart new merchantman undergoing sea trials. Sunning themselves on the afterdeck were a number of women – wives of the directors of the shipping company owning the merchantman. Grabbing the loud hailer, the Badger proceeded to comment on their personal attributes. 'There's a handy looking piece standing by that derrick – next to that old bag in the flowered hat. Look, see – that one. I could do that tubby one a bit of good an' all – I think she's waving! She is an' all – she's waving! HALLO, DOLL!! What colour you got on today then? (in an aside) *She* won't need a lifebelt – her tits'll keep *her* afloat. I suppose that bandy-legged old horror must be her mother. That bird in the jersey's not at all bad – nice pair of legs when the wind blows.' These remarks carried quite clearly to the merchantman and were heard by an important-looking gentleman with a purple face and a bowler hat, glaring from the bridge window. It turned out he was the chairman of the shipping line, married to the 'bandy-legged old horror' – who was escorted below speechless with indignation. The trawler owners made a conciliatory reply to the chairman's letter of out-raged protest and promised an enquiry. The enquiry was never made, but the loud hailer was locked away whenever the Badger was on watch.

At the same moment as the Mollies left for home a 'visitor' arrived. On the mess-deck the Tannoy came alive and Ken's voice was heard, speaking from the bridge.

'There's a pigeon on the boat-deck!'

Colin went to investigate and reported back, 'it's a racing pigeon with two rings on its leg – I reckon it's lost.'

Paddy commented, 'Jasus. If it's a thing I go for it's a lost soul.' 'That's religion for yer, you Kerry bastard,' replied the Whippit. Half the crew turned out to look at the bird which was certainly attractive. The rump and head were blue grey and the sides of the neck iridescent purple and green. His legs were coral red with a mauve bloom. One of them carried a rubber counter-mark and a numbered metal foil. The eyes were the colour of summer straw, with a pear-shaped iris.

The pigeon was nick-named Harold Wilson and was given a nylon life-line attached to a fishing rod reel, and secured gently to one leg. Having been given a dish of raisins soaked in rum essence and a shelter made from a cardboard box lined with wood-wool, Harold was left alone to recover.

Just as the light was going a freak gust of wind threw Harold off the ship and into the sea. He was pulled inboard, hand over hand, by the life-line and found to be still sitting in his shelter, which was still afloat despite being towed astern at 13 knots.

Harold refused to sit on the boat-deck after that and Colin brought him down to the galley where he settled down on a warm brick wrapped in flannel. He was content, but wary of All Sorts who came close and 'cooed' at the bird who kept one eye on the carving knife thrust in the cook's belt.

The next morning Harold was taken back on deck and placed in a sheltered area aft of the funnel. A wooden shelter filled with straw was anchored firmly to the deck and a bowl of corn flakes left inside, along with half an apple and a small tin of 'mint flavoured garden peas'. Harold ate this odd assortment settled upside down with his feet gripping the top of the shelter and his wings fully spread. After 'breakfast' the bird strutted about with a characteristic bobbing of the head and looked every bit like his name-sake. 'All he needs is a pipe,' commented the Badger. Harold spent the morning taking exercise, stopping every few steps to peck at his 'lifeline' which he finally parted. Colin sat down and made a miniature 'life-belt' from a cork fishing float. The centre hole was lined with a tiny piece of checkered horse blanket and the underside of the 'life-belt' weighted with lead pellets to provide buoyancy in the water. This fitted loosely beneath Harold's neck and was easily removed at feeding time, which seemed to be about every twenty minutes.

Harold was proving a problem as the ship was heading for inside the Arctic Circle and was due to cross the 66th parallel in a few hours. The question was whether to keep him for company and release him on the way home, or find out where he should have been going and then release him before the ice started to close in. A small majority favoured sending him on his way without delay.

The number on Harold's leg was radioed ashore by the Sparks and London replied within the hour. Harold was 'homing' to Queen's County, Ireland, having started his journey in Denmark. He was 'launched' at dawn after eating half a cabbage and a saucer of split peas soaked in water. He was back again at midday and refused to budge. At teatime he was found deep inside his shelter with his feathers fluffed up, fast asleep, standing on one leg. He was gone next morning but it's doubtful if he ever reached Queen's County. The cold would most likely have killed him.

By the late evening of the fourth day *Arctic Fox* crossed the 66th parallel of North Meridian and entered the Arctic Circle. She held her course true north and continued to behave well. The bridge compass pivoted erratically, particularly when the eye left it, as though conscious of error and intent on correcting itself before someone noticed. This caprice affected the ship, which began falling off every few minutes and refused to stand on her point until the helmsman surrendered to her whim when she quietly swung back on course.

The ice first appeared on the port quarter and then began to show up riding fast on the starboard bow. Before midnight the familiar white world had started to close in, and the cold splendour of the open ice fields crept for the first time on to the Radar screen. Twenty miles beyond the ice fields the vapour from the barrier ice drifted on the east wind which now beckoned the sea towards the land. Long before dawn the all too familiar world of the Arctic trawlerman came into sharp focus, and men's thoughts turned finally from land as their eyes made futile attempts to penetrate the empty promise of the horizon. With unconscious symbolism the galley boy lifted the flowers from off the mess-deck table and threw them into the sea (together with the cut-glass bowl) before replacing them with a large tin of salt labelled, with rare whimsy, Polar Mints.

Before the day was out *Arctic Fox* would have started fishing operations. The bridge watch would be told to stand down and the deckhands reach once more for their deck gear. Rum would be drained from bottles and obscene remarks passed about the weather. The Badger and his cronies would emerge from hibernation and Buster turn up clad in three verminous jerseys, a smock full of holes and a pair of thigh boots stamped 'Stolen from Mersey Docks and Harbour Board'. This eve-of-the-party atmosphere would be completed by Harry complaining that some lousy bastard had stolen his sou'wester and end in anti-climax when they all drifted into desultory conversation.

'There's a berg out there – a big one.'

'Any beer left, anybody?'

'Are those your boot stockings on the cat-walk?'

'You'd best tell the Chief about that gauge.'

'Which way's that berg drifting, then?'

'She's taking water all right – I've got most of it in my bunk.'

'Nor' West b' West!'

'Any beer left, Colin?'

'That's all you think about, crumpet – that and comics.'

'You can put them boot socks back an' all.'

'If you're first watch below you can mend that fire this trip.
I'm always the bastard doing it.'

'Any gash beer, Barry?'

'I'm giving it up after this trip.'

'What – crumpet?'

'That Mate's a right whiffling bastard. I did a trip with him
way back and he avoided me on landing day.'

'Who's got some gash beer – have you, Rubber Nose?'

'This Mate's all right, though.'

'If I had I'd not give you any.'

'As Mates go. He knows his job, I'll give you that.'

'Any gash rum, Badger?'

'Fuck off – you must be wrong in the head or something.'

'. . . she sat in the boozer wearing the label off this mop she'd
bought in the market – "Soak well before you squeeze" . . .'

'This cook's all right, but his bread's no good.'

'I've seen her drunk on a packet of wine gums . . .'

'For the last time I've *got* no beer left!'

The galley boy had no banter to exchange, and the conversation
of the older men didn't interest him. As dawn broke he climbed
with the extra care of the intoxicated on to the boat-deck to look
for the first time in his life upon the low Arctic in mid winter.
The wind blew icy and fresh, and pulled at his hair. The sky
changed from indigo to blue and revealed one or two pencils of
smoke on the skyline. Surrounding each was a cloud of birds.
Lying to leeward, roughly amidships, were a number of fairy

30

castles with their turrets in ruins. Passing astern was an iceberg, turquoise and emerald, which due to the erosive action of the sea was in slow dissolution. It resembled modern sculpture, and before the mist shrouded it it bowed, keeping perfect harmony with the movement of the sea. The galley boy was not to appear on the deck again for the remainder of the trip, apart from dumping rubbish over the side, and his last view of the Arctic would have to provide the stuff of memory – for he would probably never see it again. Even the memory of it was likely to be a nightmare.

On the mess-deck someone remembered it was Saturday. 'Sweethearts and Wives,' said Colin, raising his beer can. 'May they never meet,' came the customary rejoinder.

Arctic Fox rose to the crest and failed to recover. The sea topped the bulwarks as her rail dipped under.

'Who's conning this cow?'

'The Badger.'

'Need I ask!'

Rubber Nose was conning the ship, not the Badger, and Harry was steersman. He was concentrating less than usual as he was hoping to be first with a gossip-worthy piece of news.

On the bridge the radio monitor had begun its ceaseless vigil. Dozens of voices crowded the emitting stations until it sounded as though every deep water skipper had his active sender switch down. Against this familiar, incessant background the Skipper stood with his legs braced and his elbows resting on the bridge rail. Many of the voices were familiar to him, but he could have put a face to no more than a dozen. He rarely spoke on the air – it was just as rewarding to listen. Through the lies and counter lies, the red herrings and many ingenious deceptions it was occasionally possible to guess the intentions of a rival.

CHAPTER SIX

The Arctic Ocean is virtually a land-locked sea at the top of the world, 2,460 miles across and 17,850 ft. deep, maximum. Its remoteness and its size are not felt by deep water trawlermen even though land is seldom in sight for the ten days spent on the fishing grounds. If fish are present in sufficient numbers trawling is confined to a small area and the merciful darkness hides the Arctic and its constituent seas from view.

It is the turbulent seas themselves that make the life of a trawlerman such a torment in winter. Even to veer round between land and ice is difficult, because the earth's rotation deflects all free-moving bodies to the right of their original motion, whilst the sea strives to thrust them back and then forward. In this manner, gyrating and rolling, they are caught by the prevailing wind which often veers without warning – leaving the trawler trapped between tons of ice and the land.

An even greater danger is present in the drift currents. The warm waters of the Gulf Stream roll diagonally across the wide Atlantic where they meet the salt-free waters from the Polar Cap. Here, the clear blue of the Gulf Stream (temperature 57 degrees Fahrenheit) and the green Arctic Sea (temperature 32 degrees Fahrenheit) ride in folds and overlays above and below each other, maintaining a ceaseless struggle. Thrown into anger by the force of the earth's rotation and driven against the wind, their tentacles reach out to embrace the storm-beaten rocks along the eastern tip of Iceland. There they turn back across the long expanse of ocean, reaching the coast of Norway before dividing into two currents above latitude 69 degrees. One current turns north, past Bear Island and then across the Arctic Circle until it sets towards the uninhabited coast of West Spitsbergen. The other current rushes round North Cape before passing into the Barents Sea. On entering the Barents Sea, this second stream is subject to great atmospheric pressure, giving off vapour concentrations which drift in heavy thermal layers, descending finally as frozen fog. Known to trawlermen as 'Black Frost', it is easily the most feared phenomenon, bringing frostbite severe enough to require quick amputation.

Across the 900 miles of water between the coasts of Greenland and Norway never-ending storms drive relentlessly northeastwards rolling the already protesting sea into tremendous cliffs of water before it crashes in a towering crescent of foam along the rocks of the Norwegian coast.

In winter the sea thrusts deep into the hinterland of the coast before racing back to mist-enshrouded Bear Island. This lethal Atlantic serpent has many vagaries. Because of it the Arctic city of Murmansk remains Russia's only ice-free port, whereas Leningrad – much further south – is frozen solid throughout the Arctic winter. It leaves the Barents Sea navigable, and at the same time makes it possible to walk across the frozen Bosphorus.

Along the northern boundary of this forbidding area the drift-ice advances to within 60 miles of the coast of Norway, flowing fast to the west of Bear Island where it becomes pack-ice 2 ft. to 5 ft. thick. It is in this climatically savage region that some of the richest shoals of fish are to be found. Half the nation's cod, haddock, halibut, plaice and hake are caught between latitudes 73 and 77 north. Between these latitudes lies Bear Island.

This isolated Arctic island is situated 130 nautical miles south of Spitzbergen and 240 miles north of Norway. A black, snow-capped volcanic rock 68 square miles in area and without a port. There is Austervag (74 degrees 28′ North. 19 degrees 17′ East), sometimes optimistically referred to as a port. It fulfils this purpose in that it's possible to load cargo and unload stores in an adequate depth of water under sheltered conditions, but for practical purposes it remains a simple harbour. A port may possess a harbour but a harbour is not necessarily a port, and in the case of Bear Island it's never likely to become one. Bear Island is devoid of life in winter, and during January endures a temperature of minus 50 degrees Fahrenheit. Its average number of fine days in a year are less than seven and its highest peak (1,750 ft.) is rightly named Mount Misery. Its surrounding seas are its wealth.

In Elizabethan times Polar bears roamed the rocky coast and

hibernated in its sheltered crevices. Yellow Arctic poppies and white bell heather grew in profusion along the rock shelf on the southern side of the island. Gaily coloured lichens and mosses clung to the basalt along the ice-choked sounds. Being situated on the 74th parallel of north latitude, the region round Bear Island is Polar and ice is constantly to be met with – flowing swiftly on the great trans-Polar drifts and reflecting soft blue shadows against the surrounding sea. On nights free from drifting mist the Aurora Borealis gives what mariners consider its finest performance.

During the last war the rock-strewn coast and the sharp crags fringing the sea were awash with the blood and oil of two opposing navies locked in combat amid the ice-floes, and even today the ocean which pounds angrily at the base of this un-inhabited rock still yields up the crushed remains of war: perhaps the copper fore-stay wire from a submarine, or the iron deck grating from a destroyer. Some trawlers have caught aircraft in their nets, and others still trawl up barnacle-encrusted mines – alive and sensitive to vibration.

The Island figures in this narrative merely as the pivotal centre of fishing operations within the Arctic Circle. Often it was lost in darkness or glimpsed for a moment through a crystal curtain of atmospheric ice. But men knew it was there. And perhaps it is for this reason that it has wilfully claimed for itself a little more attention than it deserves.

It had taken *Arctic Fox* 5 days $3\frac{1}{2}$ hours to reach her chosen fishing ground – 1,490 miles from the United Kingdom – a distance greater than that from London to Gibraltar.

CHAPTER SEVEN

The heavy swell caught the bow as the ship eased in, and the pulse of the engine faded. As she lost way, the stem swung out in a wide arc and drifted on the cross seas. The steersman (Colin) received the order 'Steady'. In a moment or two the ship was laid to with her head into the wind. On three sides lay the great area of dark green translucent water tormented by currents circulating in the cold regions of the ocean. Bear Island bore due west two miles away. At its southern extremity lay Cape Bull, washed by the outstretched paw of the Gulf Stream as it hurried to the Arctic Sea. This forbidding place rested in glacial calm with its base pounded by driftwood and wreckage – both were plentiful. An object resembling an oil drum lay wedged in a finger of rock. Judging by the bull ring in its crown it was a depth charge.

Arctic Fox once more gathered way with the wheel hard over until the deck was sliding into the sea. The foam of her wake left a crescent of agate on the surface. She circumnavigated the Island and came to a stop west of Mount Misery. It was here that she felt the full force of the drift currents. The wind and tide were setting fully ashore, then racing in a confused trend to the south before turning back north with what could only be described as tireless malice.

If *Arctic Fox* stayed where she was she would be turned across the sea or caught in a vortex from which she would be lucky to escape. Although they could not be seen on Radar, there were rocks just for'ard of the beam, and in the current she could quickly be set ashore.

Colin stood rigid, and resisted what must have been the very natural temptation to glance to starboard. He was an inquisitive bastard at the best of times.

Once more the ship got under way and steamed roughly parallel to the east coast. She was attempting to 'find bottom' by using her echo sounder before launching her trawl into the sea. Once a stable area had been found and the fathom depth confirmed by means other than the unreliable charts, she would start her run up on to the fishing ground. *Arctic Fox's* knowledgeable crew could plot every movement of their ship, sense her change of direction, predict the pulse beat of her engine, without stirring from their bunks. They knew with great accuracy where they were, but there was one thing they didn't know. At what time would *Arctic Fox* shoot away?

Meanwhile, the ship laid a course to the open sea and stood

on this course for a cable or more. Having come up into the wind she eased in to 4 knots before laying broadside on athwart the Island. The sounder confirmed the jagged profile of the ocean bed, and *Arctic Fox* moved away from the land. With so little way on, the ship was slow to answer the helm and she had to be opened up to 6 knots before she obeyed the rudder. Her bow went under as the wheel went over, and Bear Island passed astern on the weather side.

Ice was forming on the surface of the ocean as *Arctic Fox* altered course to continue her search. On the foredeck all was prepared. Strands and grummets were put in places where they could be snatched up in an emergency. Cowhide pennants were cut and ready soaking in barrels. The bobbins were newly reeved and the trawl cut free of its lashings, but still secured at intervals to prevent it being swept over the side.

Colin eased the wheel a few spokes as the ship paid off, and soon she stood on her point. An hour passed, and danger took a pace or two nearer. The familiar and ceaseless routine would soon begin. The wind veered unexpectedly, and for a moment or two Bear Island, now astern, was clearly visible with her peaks brushing the clouds.

The clouds parted, and the diamond-studded sky was briefly visible. The Great Bear constellation lay on the meridian above the Pole. By following the curved tail of the Bear backwards away from the Pole Star it was possible to see Arcturus, which apart from the significance of its name is the second brightest star in northern latitudes. This was the only time it remained visible long enough for a bearing to be taken and, by way of farewell, the Northern Lights laid a ladder of light across the sea. Then the clouds closed in, and all was darkness once more.

By supper time the decks were quilted with snow, and minute spicules of ice were falling from out of the night.

CHAPTER EIGHT

It was something both physical and chemical. Starting in the engine room – they seemed to catch it first. Then taken up by the cook and repeated to anyone within ear-shot by the galley boy. (Mates usually remain silent and bosuns look busy and won't answer.) But everyone felt the tension rising. 'The old man's going to shoot the trawl.' Some gave latitude to these predictions and said, 'By tea time, I should think'. The bridge watch who had been closest to the Skipper during the day were more precise. 'We shoot away at midnight if the old man finds bottom' or 'if the reports are good'. Midnight came and went, and *Arctic Fox* ploughed on into the darkness. At 3 a.m. the Skipper unstoppered the engine room speaking tube and whistled.

'Chief? Shooting in 15 minutes!'

The Skipper half turned round and glanced at the supersonic echo meter, its pen recording regular traces on the iodine-impregnated paper. The sounder indicated the bed of the ocean was 200 fathoms beneath *Arctic Fox's* keel, free of contours and devoid of gulleys. The Mate entered the bridge. The Skipper looked up and said:

'Ken, get one of the watch to haul the log.'

'Aye Aye,' replied the Mate.

'Shoot in a quarter of an hour,' added the Skipper.

'Right,' answered the Mate, dashing off the bridge.

The Skipper gave a corrected course to the man at the wheel so that the trawler would stay in the same depth of water during towing, and then dismissed the helmsman as the Sparks appeared on the bridge to take the wheel and hold the course steady. The Skipper crossed to the Radar and looked down inside the rubber viewing hood. The range showed 60 miles, and the sweep was clear of ships, land or obstructions.

Arctic Fox was alone.

The seconds ticked by. It was nearly time. All hands appeared on deck fully rigged. Except the Whippit, who wore his thigh boots on the wrong feet and had failed to find his sou'wester, though he *had* managed to grab a pot of tea and a banjo. The Whippit had a clear eye for priorities! The trawl was cut free of its lashings. Two deckhands took up positions beneath the bridge, facing the winch. The Mate stood beside them. The Badger and Paddy made their way to the fore gallows to man the door. Cliff and Buster did the same aft, with the deckie learner beside them. Pete and Ron took up station midships, portside, ready to control the wires for the Yo-Yo, Fanny and Gilson. The Whippit was beside the starboard winch barrel facing aft ready to heave on the after gilson when needed.

The two hundred feet of the *Arctic Fox* came slowly broadside to the wind. The sea swept over the low freeboard and bounded along as far as the quarter-deck. The bridge telegraph rang as the Skipper swung the handle which transmits the signal to the engine room. The handle was upright at 'Stop'. Men stood quite still – and waited. The Mate flicked his cigarette stub over the side. The Whippit bit into his banjo and looked at his feet with surprise. For the first time, the deckmen were a unified crew, a feeling that would grow stronger as the days passed, a feeling that would manifest itself in the deckies' traditional dislike of the engineers, and the Sparks in particular, as none of these men shared the discomfort of the rest of the crew out on the deck and were not exposed to the weather and the danger it brings.

The Cod End was swinging above the gunwhale of the ship. The Skipper crossed the bridge to starboard and leaned out of the window looking both fore and aft, and after a few moments' deliberation gave his first command.

'Cod End outboard! LET GO!!'

The end of the trawl plummeted into the sea. From the bridge window the Skipper half inclined his body and reached back far enough to grip the telegraph without taking his eyes off the deck. He threw the handle down and rang his ship on 'Slow Ahead'.

By this time the Sparks had put the wheel over, and slowly the ship began to obey the screw. The heavy iron bobbins crashed into the sea. The trawl began to float away, the headline went over the side. A crescent of air-filled aluminium floats pulled hard against the swell. *Arctic Fox* rolled to a stop and went astern a few revolutions, allowing time for the trawl to spread over the surface of the water before it sank finally and was lost from view. The winchmen released the brakes, both warps ran out and then stopped. The fore door was released and crashed into the sea, followed by the after door. The warps were paid out through the bollards. *Arctic Fox* cleaved the water 'Slow Ahead', towing her trawl at a depth of 25 fathoms astern of the trawler. The can line with its marker float, the last visible sign of £5,000 worth of gear and net, had disappeared. The Skipper threw down the handle of the telegraph 'Full Ahead'. The Sparks brought the wheel back to midships. All hands were now clear of the deck except the two winchmen and the Mate. The winch started to pay out the warp, both drums turning, each winchman keeping one hand on the break and one eye on the warp snaking out in front of him – watching for the 'fathom marks' served through the strands of both warps at 25 or 50 fathom intervals. *Arctic Fox* will be towing in 200 fathoms, and the winchmen must now pay out warp equal to three times the depth of water to allow the iron bobbins reeved on to the ground wire to travel over the bed of the sea at the right tension.

As the last of the fathom marks disappeared into the sea the brakes were applied to the winch and *Arctic Fox* again came to a stop. The crew rushed back on to the deck. The foredoorman (Paddy) dragged the messenger from the quarter-deck to the foredeck, climbed over the pound boards and leaned over the starboard rail waiting for the next command.

'HOOK ON!' bellowed the Skipper.

Paddy hooked the messenger wire on to the fore warp which was now taut alongside the rail and released it on the command 'LET GO!' The slack wire leading aft was thrown overboard by Cliff and Buster standing midships. The Skipper put the wheel over three points, and *Arctic Fox* turned a few degrees to port allowing her starboard rail to come close alongside both warp wires which were then in line to be joined by the fast descending messenger hook.

Once the hook met the after warp, the Bosun (Barry) shouted

directions to the bridge so that *Arctic Fox* could lead both wires into the open jaws of the towing block. With both warps together in the block, the jaw was banged shut and the block pin pushed home and secured by a half hitch. The Whippit had gathered up the slack and the messenger hook was lifted off the warp, hauled back off the winch drum and coiled on the quarter-deck.

Barry leaned over the rail and watched astern of the trawler and then after a moment or two turned and shouted to the bridge.

'All square, and level aft!'

The Skipper nodded, and then returned the telegraph to 'Half Ahead'. Finally, he checked the sounder which read 206 fathoms. The ocean bed had sloped slightly, the chart would indicate in which direction. With the depth stabilised and the warps towing at the correct angle, the trawl was now travelling the sea bed. The two doors were diverting the warps at an angle favourable to the continued spread of the trawl. The Dan Lenos were rolling on the bottom, weighing down the lower lip, the mouth being kept open by the buoyancy of the floats. The ocean was now being raked for an area of 120 yards, the span being governed by the length of the bridles shackled to the doors. In three hours the trawl would have covered a distance of about 10 nautical miles.

This arduous and dangerous operation had taken less than 7 minutes to complete and would be repeated day and night, in fair weather and foul, for as long as the trawler stayed at the fishing grounds. Three hours passed.

Hauling time. The engine room bell rang three times. Rubber Nose and Colin, both on Watch Duty, were fully rigged and ran around calling the deckmen from their berths, then raced on to the deck ready to obey the first command from the bridge which would start in motion the machinery and muscle power needed to haul the trawl which lies one cable astern of the ship riding on its bobbins and lancasters on the bed of the Arctic Ocean.

On the bridge, the Skipper moved continuously between the Radar scanner, the echo sounder and the starboard window. Watching the sea with a look of distrust and glancing aft to check the angle of the warps and then back once more to check the depth line on the sounder. There was no horizon, the sea was running a heavy swell and the wind was blowing from the north. Rubber Nose 'shipped up' the winch by pushing the engaging lever forward and banging the clutch lever over to 'heave'. Colin stood on the quarter-deck holding the 14 lb. hammer ready to 'knock-out' – strike the pin out of the towing block. With a slow, graceful movement *Arctic Fox* bore away so that the warps would not foul the screw as the towing block was released. The rest of the deckhands appeared, ready to take up their positions – the same as for 'shooting'.

Arctic Fox came slowly broadside to the wind as the sea danced along the rail and cascaded over the deckmen whose movements glistened from the spray which now fell over them. The emerald sea foamed and boiled along the deck as *Arctic Fox* rolled gently on the swell. The Skipper suddenly reappeared at the bridge window and shouted a command.

'LEGGO!'

The command was acknowledged.

'AYE AYE!'

Colin swung the hammer and struck the towing block, forcing the pin out. The two warps parted from the block with tremendous force and instantly adopted their natural angle from the sheaves atop of the gallows. The bridge telegraph rang for half speed and then again for 'Stop'. The wheel went over 20 degrees. The winch drums slowly gathered speed and groaned with the weight of the trawl.

The ship rolled in sympathy, shuddered with the strain, and finally adopted the motion of a rocking horse. The winch kept turning. The warp wires built up quickly on the drum. The winchmen forced the guiding on wheels over, first to port and then back again to ensure the even lay of the wires. Now both warps were vertical in the sea and whipping with the strain. Next the doors came up, dripping with brine. Both warps were now still in the gallows sheave. The winch had stopped. Fore and aft, the cowhide pennants were made free and chains thrown round both doors and secured to cleats attached to the gallows frame. With both doors secured, the winch was eased forward to gather up the slack bridles and to bring both Dan Lenos up from the depths. The wires extending from the after top wing were parted at the 'G' link and connected to a similar 'G' link on the after gilson, whose wire was served through sheaves along the engine room casing, its free end held by a few turns around the starboard winch barrel ready to heave when the order was given. The line of cans broke the surface ahead of the submerged trawl and rode on the swell like a giant necklace. Suddenly, the Cod End shot up and all eyes turned to watch it. The net was now drifting lazily along the side of the ship and was pulled in over the side by hand as and when the swell allowed. The groundwire came inboard with its giant 26 in. bobbins and rubber lancasters, and crashed into its position under the rail. Beckets were secured round the body of the trawl by the Mate and the belly was hoisted by the Fanny, controlled by the wireman (the Whippit). Finally, the Cod End was girdled by the halving becket and dragged clear of the water by the fore gilson. The Cod End crashed against the bag ropes. The Mate waited for the trawler to roll to port and then gave the wireman the order to 'Lower'. This procedure which is potentially dangerous (many men have been crushed or maimed under the Cod End which can weigh up to 2 tons) has remained unchanged for a century and is easily the Mate's most exacting task during his gruelling time on the deck. If the wireman, Pete, responsible for lifting this mass from the sea and guiding it in over the side of the vessel allows his wire to take a riding turn, starts to surge and then suddenly lets go, the Mate would be killed by the weight of fish falling on top of him.

The Mate stepped forward, leaned away and gripped the restraining knot of the Cod End with both hands. The draw line tightened and the knot untied. From a height of three feet the fish crashed on to the deck and thundered into the pounds. Hauling was complete. There was silence everywhere on the deck as the men looked at the fish in the pound. Disappointment showed clearly on their faces. The tow was a failure. Lying in the pound was eight kit ($\frac{1}{2}$ ton) of codling, mixed with mock halibut, sand eels and other unsaleable fish.

CHAPTER NINE

All through that night and for most of the following day *Arctic Fox* towed along the south-east side of Bear Island. As the trawl came up empty and was shot away again, the crew stared fixedly at the bridge – making their wordless protest. The Skipper stared back in the same manner. This was a game without words and both sides knew the rules. A bad start and a good finish often went together in their experience, but there was no harm in letting the old man see they wanted action.

There was another adage they were sure to mention before long: 'Heavy weather, heavy fishing.' But the prevailing weather was anything but heavy. It was winter, and this was the Arctic, so the ice and wind would be along soon. By the time the last traces of oil from the midship's fuel point had been washed clean by the sea the Arctic would live up to its name. The sea and sky would dissolve one into the other and Mount Misery, only a mile away, would vanish from the Radar behind the curtain of a blizzard.

All trawlers are manned by weather prophets, and *Arctic Fox* had twenty of them. Not one of them *wanted* bad weather, but each tried to out-do the other in the gloom of his forecast – with the desperate hope of a man alone on a life-raft. If a storm blew up, everyone chanted, 'I said it would'. If the wind dropped to a whisper, the fact passed without notice or was greeted with, 'Always fines away like this before a gale'. Fatalists to a man – and remembering that if they anticipated the worst before it happened they were sure to be in the right camp – they peered with fearful pleasure at the weather and snarled back at the optimist who thought it looked quite promising with, 'Just you wait and see'.

At ten o'clock in the morning, with the gutting finished and two hours to go before hauling time, the card school turned down the tops of their thigh boots, pulled off their frocks and mufflers and returned to the mess-deck to resume play. An old blanket was thrown across the mess-deck table, money tipped out of tobacco tins, fags were 'bent on', pots of tea appeared, busters were stuffed with pickles or jam – and Buster dealt the cards. Harry didn't play cards, and felt aggrieved that no one would be left to argue with him, so he complained out loud to himself.

'Ashore they don't know what it's like to come out this way. Easy to ignore what you can't see and don't know about. Human nature. Stands to reason – hardships what affects you, not the other bloke. Now if I was a sick dog people I'd never heard of would send me "Get Well" cards and bones tied up with ribbon. It's true!'

'Shut up, you gobbie bastard, we're trying to play cards.'

Buster raked the money across the blanket using the lid of a tobacco tin. It was a familiar gesture to anyone who had played cards with him, and silence fell as each player tried to remember Buster's system of play and at what stage in the game he had outwitted them. Buster had no system, only a strong instinct for the game and an understanding of the people he was playing with. He simply knew how each member of the crew would bet and this was a clear pointer to what cards they held. By keeping a straight face to hide the weakness of his own cards he 'raised' accordingly, and bluffed heavily when his hand was feeble. Buster was not so much a player as a gambler who believed chance was not an unbeatable factor. From the strength of this conviction he gained a controlling influence which kept him ahead of the game. He was certainly the finest Stud Poker player from amongst *Arctic Fox's* crew, and the beginner needed several skills besides that of a straight face to thwart Buster's iron grip on their money. His expertise was evident the moment he started to play. Beginning with a spectacular waterfall shuffle he placed the pack face down whilst each player bet an equal amount. After the deal – too fast for the eye to record – he would lean back with the tips of his fingers resting against the edge of the table and his eyes burning into the remaining players. After the deal they bet again, and at this point Buster slowly gathered in his five cards and gave them a brief, disinterested glance. From then on he watched every movement on the faces of the players and was raking the money across the table before they were even aware that they had lost it.

If we accept the view that gambling is the one way to buy hope on credit Buster's inscrutable play left no one hoping for very long.

From a number of 'improving' tracts left around the ship by religious performers, one was pinned up on Buster's side of the table and another above the heads of the players facing him. Buster's tract read: 'Discretion stamps a value upon all our qualities. It instructs us to make use of them to our own advantage.' The tract on the other side of the table read: 'If we lay no restraint upon our vices they will hurry us into ruin and misery.'

With sighs and oaths his opponents stretched their legs under the mess-deck table and stared silently at the ceiling. 'Another game, gentlemen?' His tone was judicial, but friendly. The victims nodded – and were soon on their way to another beating. For entertainment Buster would draw a Royal Flush from the newly shuffled pack – usually at the third or fourth attempt. The chances of being *dealt* five cards of one suit running Ace, King, Queen, Jack, Ten, have been computed at 700,000 to 1. When Buster first demonstrated this daunting piece of card play there were cries of, 'I know how he does it! The key cards have bent corners!' Buster would silently break the seal on a new deck and after a few tries once more produce a Royal Flush. After that the rest of the school would try for themselves, but none of them ever succeeded and Buster never showed them how to. With his tobacco tin stuffed full of £1 notes he considered he'd done enough to break the monotony of life on board his 'floating card school', and the secrets of the game were useful only if they remained exclusive.

Arctic Fox made her abrupt, rhythmic curtsey to the waves, and with her head to wind continued towing the Granton Trawl at 3 knots. The telegraph rang on 'Half Ahead'. The wind freshened a little and then fined away. Suddenly it came back, driving little bullets of ice across the foredeck. Again it dropped, this time to a whisper, and then rose to a steady 30 knots, orchestrating the rigging and ratlines of the ship and causing the derricks both fore and aft to veer – although they were lashed tight up and as secure as deft hands could make them. As the wind rose the temperature dropped – almost imperceptibly at first – and then as the snow began covering the ship the glass touched zero, wavered and then continued to fall. *Arctic Fox* had stopped her curtsey. Now she buried her bow at each successive wave, rolled heavily and tossed her stern upwards to the black sky. On the mess-deck the sidelights were already securely bolted to the scuttles, and now the deadlights were shut and each secured by its clips to the watertight porthole. The fiddle battens were replaced on the mess-deck table to stop food being flung about. Bottles, and anything that might smash or roll about, were laid flat or wedged tight. The card game ended and the players scattered.

The sea was now running a heavy swell, crashing over the whaleback and down on to the foredeck in a brilliant, cruel display of force and grandeur before it ran out through the scuppers, all aquamarine and pearl. Gale force eight, freshening to strong gale nine. The wind intensified to 40 knots, filling the lungs with minute stilettos of ice and freezing the sensitive muscles each side of the mouth. Ice, too, covered the winch, froze the lifeboats solid in their davits, thickened the rigging and welded every wire into its sheave or pulley block. The waves were now sweeping in towards the vessel in a wide, lethal crescent of green sea, touching 30 ft. in height. The temperature, too, had fallen, and stood at minus 39 degrees Fahrenheit – 71 degrees below freezing point. The air was now colder than the sea and the dreaded Black Frost began to rise from the surface until vitrified water hung everywhere in the freezing air like amorphous black glass. The masts were sugar candy – ice blue and strangely beautiful. Spray froze on the underside of the ship's rail into long points of ice, looking like fairy dragon's teeth in endless array.

Arctic Fox heeled over. The starboard rail went under and the sea roared on to the deck, flushing the piss in the scuppers and fusing the lights shining on the towing block. The Radar scanner, gyrating on the bridge top, ground to a stop – frozen.

Visibility was nil to one cable. The ship was blind. *Arctic Fox* had encountered – somewhat earlier than expected – the first of her misfortunes.

The Chief Engineer, called from his bunk by the voice pipe on the bridge, stood on the engine room grating watching the revolution counter as the stern heaved out of the water and the screw raced. 'To keep her steady at 3 knots we're having to burn fuel for at least $12\frac{1}{2}$. That's no good at all at this early stage of the trip,' he shouted with his head inside the sound-proof hood which housed the telephone. 'I reckon she's taking water somewhere.'

The two men on watch closed the half door on the starboard quarter-deck, then made their way forward along the lea side to cut a cow-hide pennant for the after door and put cans on a new top wing which the daymen should have bolshed out ready. But it wouldn't surprise either of them if this hadn't been done. Daymen, in their opinion, did little but sit under the whaleback and drink cans of beer, and wait for the Mate to go watch below – the signal for everyone to file aft and lie about on the mess-deck until the Bosun, looking up from his cod ends and finding he was all alone on the deck, turned them out again – with loud curses and threats ranging from complete castration to downright blackmail. Slowly and with difficulty they made their way across the foredeck, grasping the stanchions whilst their feet found purchase on the deck which gave every sign of sliding into the sea. As the ship rose to meet each fresh encounter with the waves, they ran forward until under the shelter of the whaleback. The Skipper's alert face could be seen watching them through the curtain of water flung to the bridgetop, falling in a solid sheet on to the ice-covered winch where it froze into long pointed fingers.

The watchmen kicked the wedges out to free the hatch bars and removed the tarpaulin to expose the wooden covers. With practised ease they balanced on the coaming before descending quickly the vertical iron ladder to the hold. They stood either side of the ladder base and held on to the red painted boards of the net bins running along both sides of the hold. The thud and boom of the sea was loudest here, and rose to a metallic ring as the bows lurched downwards with each new wave. The two men were now below the waterline, and for a few seconds there was a dull silence as the ship recovered and the waves rolled towards the stern. They moved along, each looking for a coil of bolsh until both stood side by side on the hatch covering the descent to the locker which housed the anchor cable. Without speaking, each took hold of a lifting ring and raised the two halves of the wooden cover. Before their eyes had grown accustomed to the black hold below them they heard a sound which told them their instincts had been right. Reaching down inside, their fingers touched icy water. Striking a match they crouched low, hoping not to see what they knew to be there. A thousand miles from home, heading due north into an Arctic gale, the ship had sprung a leak!

Leaving the cover off they climbed hurriedly back up the iron ladder and out on to the deck which was now submerged under the impact from successive waves. Quickly, and with experienced movements, they ran across the deck as the ship rose from between the crests. They stood on the raised platform behind the winch as the sea roared over the rail and boiled in a white fury as far back as the quarter-deck. As the ship rose again from the hollows they ran for the bridge ladder and the safety of the boat-deck. The Skipper himself opened the bridge door and dragged both men inside. He was about to hear something he had no reason to expect, as the ship had been in dry dock only days before her departure.

In quick succession *Arctic Fox* had suffered the second of her misfortunes.

CHAPTER TEN

The Mate clutched his way aft to make his report to the Skipper. As *Arctic Fox* took yet another sea, he clutched the winch barrel and flung out his left leg so as to gain purchase on the winch grating. As the deck tilted to 45 degrees the hard ridge of muscle across the back of his shoulders flexed against the strain. Within a minute, *Arctic Fox* righted herself and the Mate relaxed his grip ready to dash for the bridge ladder and safety. Before he could do so, he had to free his left boot which had frozen to the deck.

The water in the forehold had neither affected the trim of the *Arctic Fox* nor reduced her speed. Hoses were immediately joined up and the donkey started and lowered into the hold, but only a small trickle of water had been sucked out after an age of waiting. It might only be a rivet missing from one of the plates below the waterline, but if the water rose faster than it could be pumped out it would inevitably find its way back below decks and flood the fishroom.

And with successive waves, equal in force to a probable 6,000 pounds per square foot, striking the bows, the danger of other rivets becoming displaced was a real one. As the long, fruitless day ended the question of the flooding became the main topic of conversation. It was to stay in the mind like a dull ache right up to the end. Dockyard mateys would have flinched had they heard what trawlermen thought of them. It takes a lot to make a dockyard matey flinch . . .

On the evening of the seventh day at sea the wind stayed firmly in the east for hours on end and drift ice began to appear, riding the wave crests before plunging into the hollows. *Arctic Fox* held her course steady against the fetch of the wind, but the ice made it difficult to hold a straight tow, and the trawl needed split-second timing at hauling time.

By way of compensation, *Arctic Fox* caught seventy baskets of fish, most of it cod. In the pound the gutting started immediately. There was a kind of weary pleasure in the size of the haul, for the first reserves of energy were being used up. Even so it would be another eight days before the Skipper hauled for the last time, brought *Arctic Fox's* doors in, lashed the trawl alongside and turned her round and headed for home.

The singing began. The Bosun chooses most of the songs with the care of a well-bred archivist. There were those for gutting, those for washing down when the gutting was finished and those for going aft at the end. If the Skipper was on the bridge, and in a bad mood, there was a song for him, too.

> 'Oh, dear Skipper, is it true
> You can't get a crew to sail with you?
> BYE – BYE – BASTARD!'

As the bridge window banged in disgust there would be roars of laughter, good strong laughter – but free from malice.

The Mate was also treated to a ditty if he happened to be taking over the bridge.

> 'Gee, but it's great when you get to come Mate
> All on the bridge on your own
> Harmonising a song as you tow her along
> Towing your baby through foam.'

Foam, however, was not the appropriate word on this occasion. For *Arctic Fox* had run into pack ice. The Skipper altered course to regain clear water, and then hauled round to get back on the tow. With this difficult manoeuvre completed a new hazard appeared.

'Iceberg on the port bow!' yelled the Bosun, raising his cupped hands in the direction of the bridge.

It was indeed an iceberg. The deckhands gave it a disinterested, critical glance – more concerned with judging its probable size and assessing its centre of gravity than anything else. It had come, most probably, from Greenland, where ice descends to the sea in glaciers from which icebergs split off and float away – ice castles 150 ft. high, girdled with foam, floating like jewels until they reach warm water where they begin to melt, change their orbital centre and roll over in the process.

The berg was 20 fathoms off the bow, floating serene on the surface of the sea. Its bounding lines, its edges, stiletto-sharp and beautifully lethal, burned in a prism of fire and seemed to beckon. Turning slowly, so that the searchlights caught a new facet, its peak exploded into fragments and then splintered into chipped icicles of light. It floated by – near enough to be touched with the aid of a short haul – and passed in majesty and in death along the side of the ship and then astern.

The Skipper called for the Mate who was below decks in the fish room.

'I want you on the bridge, Ken.'

The Mate bounded up the bridge ladder and hurried on to the bridge.

The Skipper spoke without turning round.

'I can't ease her in, you realise that. Not while we're towing. I know what everyone's thinking, but we're here to make a living, Ken. Without fish there's no justification.'

The Skipper turned to face the Mate.

'None at all, is there? And now we've found fish!'

The Mate stayed silent.

The Skipper continued, facing the Mate but avoiding his gaze.

'I want you to post two of the watch as look-out in the bows. I know it's a fucking awful job, Ken, but the ship's blind. I can't see what we're going into.'

He handed the Mate a message which the 'Sparks' had just taken down in morse.

LARGE BERG 150 FT. HIGH ENCIRCLED WITH DEBRIS. STOP. VISUAL SIGHTING OF FOUR GROWLERS. STOP. TWO LARGE BERGS LOW IN WATER. STOP. ONE HALF MILE AHEAD YOUR PRESENT COURSE AT 15.36 HUNDRED HOURS. STOP.

'Anything else?' said the Mate, unable to keep the rancour out of his voice.

'Yes, send Paddy to take the wheel.'

Already the two men on watch had climbed out of the pound

51

and run forward. They now stood crouching in the bows staring into a black wall, watching for the sudden appearance of something that was not black. A cloud of vapour fell instantly upon them and started to freeze their outer clothing solid. The four gloved hands that gripped the rail were soon welded to it by ice. Paddy at the wheel held his course blindly. One point deviation would fling his two shipmates to their death. For a while they noticed nothing, and then they saw a mass of ice coming towards them, dead ahead. Six growlers, followed by two solitary icebergs. Beyond them, drifting silent and alone, a jagged cliff of ice 150 ft. high, turning slowly in the black night. A floating island of death glistening with spurs, its submerged base an estimated eight times larger than the volume showing above the surface.

Just at that moment a grey, foaming mass of sea towered above them and flung them back to the ladder top where they turned over and over. They picked themselves up and raced for shelter.

Colin clutched the port winch drum and screamed at the bridge.

'DEAD AHEAD! DEAD AHEAD! DEAD AHEAD!'

He yelled it again with all the power in his lungs, his free arm pointing towards the bows.

At that moment there was a sudden explosion ahead of the ship. One that echoed and reverberated across the Arctic wastes, bounced back off distant, unseen cliffs and rolled with a hollow roar across the surface of the sea, plunged into the depths and rose again in a shattering tide of sound. *Arctic Fox* staggered and veered wildly as the echo died with a long, wounded moan.

The giant berg had exploded in *Arctic Fox's* path. Its remains fell back into the night in a raging cloud of vapour and foam.

'Starboard your helm!' roared the Skipper.

Paddy spun the wheel hard over.

'Where away' roared the Skipper from the open window of the bridge.

His voice failed to carry on the wind. With the Tannoy he tried again.

'WHERE AWAY? TAKE A LOOK, COLIN, WHERE AWAY?'

Colin rushed to the rail and peered for'ard.

'All clear ahead – ALL CLEAR AHEAD, ALL CLEAR AHEAD!'

For some time afterwards the retina of the eye still held a vision of this encounter with Death. A beautiful thing, sparkling with polished cruelty. Predictably, the Sparks referred to it as 'she'. Predictably, he was the only one who showed any fear.

Arctic Fox's avoiding action had been taken just in time and she missed the icebergs, although she collided with one of the growlers which buckled her port rail midships and swept all the reserve coal (for the galley fire) off the boat deck and into the sea. The trawl had gone also, or if recovered, would be a total loss. By putting the helm hard over, the axis of direction had been abruptly altered and as a consequence the trawl would have capsized. There was only one thing to do – haul and find out.

The Skipper brought *Arctic Fox* starboard to windward, allowing the ship to drift across the line of tow. As she came leeward of her course, the raging sea was calmed a little by the lateral drift of the ship. The searchlights picked out the warps which lay close together – a bad sign! The deckhands took up their duty positions. The Skipper watched, but gave no orders. The Mate was now in control.

The doors came up, followed by the headline. The net had been torn to pieces. The belly, square, and one top wing all floated in ribbons and had been ripped away from the headline from which most of the cans were missing. Both grummets had parted and the Cod End drifted on the swell. It contained about 5 baskets of fish, some of them falling out of the torn mesh and trailing on the surface of the sea with their white bellies uppermost. Some of the larger cod thrashed the water in an attempt to regain the depths, and were thrust back by the density of the water and the air in their bodies. The sea, their element, refused to have them back. The deckhands looked at the trawl with dismay. Only the gulls were gratified.

Within an hour a new trawl had been fitted and *Arctic Fox* was ready to shoot away once again. But . . .

Visibility was less than three cables, and standing direct in *Arctic Fox's* path was another iceberg.

The Skipper leapt to the handle of the telegraph and swung it round to Full Speed Astern, shouting at the same time to Paddy to put the rudder hard a port. Down in the engine room the second engineer and fireman worked with fanatical speed to reverse the ship but they were too late. The berg stopped and waited for *Arctic Fox* to strike. Two vice-like jaws of ice extended out from it, and the summit was raised up into pinnacles and turrets. As it rolled, fangs protruded from below the water line.

Arctic Fox struck. Below decks the boilers broke free of their restraining straps and the auxiliary dynamo was torn from its bed. Water poured into the steering flat beneath the poop and the toothed quadrant which engaged the rudder lay flooded in the after wheel-house. Main-steam dropped and the gauges fell back. The pumps stopped. The draught fans stopped and one furnace blew back. The main engine was stopping as the ship climbed to the sky. Then there was stillness. There was no escaping steam, no rushing feet. Just silence.

Arctic Fox had struck a glancing blow to one of the submerged spurs, and when the avalanche of water subsided her bows were found to be intact. The Skipper's first remark was defensive.

'Why didn't someone see that berg?'

Barry and the Mate arrived breathless on the bridge, almost before the ice had finished crashing down on to the fore-head.

'What happened?'

'That berg suddenly swung in front of us.'

The Mate looked reproachful, but said nothing. It was the Skipper who was obliged to take up the conversation.

'Barry, take all those not on watch below and tackle the flooding aft. Ken, grab a couple of the lads and take a good look at the bow and whaleback. Clear the ice best you can and see what the score is.'

The anchor had fouled on the berg but broke free as the ship drifted away on the swell. The flukes, however, were still embedded and the cable was running out fast as the iceberg drifted away with the four ton anchor.

To keep the anchor secure in the hawse pipe hand brakes had been screwed down tightly on the gypsies soon after leaving port.

54

In addition, the cable had been lashed with anchor dogs secured to chains, and the spurling gate filled in with cement to prevent the sea from entering the chain locker. All this had been wrenched out and smashed by the impact.

The ship was now anchored to the iceberg at the end of a free-running cable. As the berg was heavier than the ship it took her in tow and swung to the south at 5 knots. *Arctic Fox* stopped her engines and followed, an unwilling captive. She rang on 'Slow Ahead', and steam was brought to the anchor windlass. *Arctic Fox* closed with the berg, drawing her cable as she went. Slowly, a foot at a time, she crept up to the 50 foot high berg turning and rolling in the clear green water.

Barry took the wheel and placed the bows between two jagged spurs for the run-up. On the instant of command, the ship was put into reverse and she stopped three feet from the face of the berg. The flukes were agitated free and the anchor lifted clear by the fore Gilson. It was laid on the fore-head and the cable flaked out around it. Speed was essential. As the Mate, Colin and Yorkie worked to clear the whaleback of ice boulders and secure the anchor, the sea was visibly freezing. Hard grains of driven snow built up round their boots and froze there. Their frocks were soon rigid with frozen spray. It took three hours to complete the operation and it is doubtful if they could have remained on the exposed forepeak for much longer.

Arctic Fox rode free. The compass faltered, and then began its swing until she cleared to the open sea. Despite the weather she continued to strike due north. Direct to the Pole.

CHAPTER ELEVEN

Arctic Fox's plight was not a happy one. Having changed her fishing ground she was now in an area not fully charted. There was nowhere to run for shelter. She was still blind and perceptibly down by the head due to the water in her forehold. She had tons of ice on her weather side, which not even steam hoses could shift. Her aerials were iced up and the wind against the weight of the trawl she was towing made it hourly more difficult to keep her head up into the wind. With visibility at 3 cables, and without Radar, she couldn't avoid the icebergs brought down by the currents because the watch wouldn't see them in time. If she stopped she would be in danger of being trapped by pack ice, or struck by 'blinders' (small icebergs) which cannot be seen in such weather. This, combined with a sustained 40 knot wind and low temperature, could lead to disaster. The wind continued to fling spray over the ship up to her bridge top, where it froze on top of ice already there. Ice was also descending from the atmosphere in the form of Black Frost and freezing men where they stood.

No one saw the self-inflating life rafts torn from their cradles and swept off the boatdeck. And as the boatdeck itself was buried in ice it took a long time before the remaining two were dug out and their quick release attachments made serviceable. These two were adequate to carry the crew if the ship were abandoned, which was just as well because no one had the least faith in the two old-fashioned wooden lifeboats.

At seven o'clock the ship was still icing up, still going north. There was continuous snow and ice on the weather side. Every man aboard grabbed something. Axe, marline spike, spanners, hammer, even snatch blocks were used to get the ship back on to an even keel. The work was slow and dangerous, and even to take a glove off could result in lost fingers.

The crew attacked the ice for more than an hour. It resisted their efforts and continued to build up. For the first time, men talked openly of the ship turning over.

At about seven thirty in the morning steam trawler *Arctic Fox* registry G.Y. 746 started going over to starboard and a tense Sparks stood by the morse key ready to call for help. By eight o'clock *Arctic Fox* recorded a list of 30 degrees. By nine it was 34 degrees.

As men looked up and reacted to what they saw, what they felt, what they knew could happen . . . many things bit into the memory. The Mate, attacking the ice with private fury until the axe disintegrated and chips of metal flew everywhere. The useless courage of Wacker's remark, 'It looks like goodbye'. Gloved hands bright blue above the wrist. The Badger grinning with rage as his great bulk flung itself at the ice – a memorable exercise in frustration. A gannet standing frozen dead on the rail of the boat deck, its wings half open for flight. Men falling into each others' arms, driven there by the destroying wind that thrust their breath back down their throats. A falcon dying – proud in death, too proud to be so ironically defeated. Colin screaming at the ship, 'Founder, you cow, bloody well founder!' in a strange mixture of defiance and compassion.

By midday things were about the same. The ship was shapeless and dead, buried under winter's malice. There had to be a limit to human endurance. Who would be the first to crack and rush for his life-jacket? Buster came first to mind, but everyone knew Harry would be the one. Harry would die like the rest, but not from drowning. Harry would be wearing a life-jacket. The Mate watched him with cold scrutiny. At one o'clock the hull groaned and gently, quietly, the decks began sliding into the sea. It looked like goodbye. Barry and Paddy fell against each other and laughed. A contact with humanity. No one wanted to be alone now. Rubber Nose joked. 'What will the enquiry say? There'll be no evidence.' Everyone. laughed. These were not men who didn't want to live any longer. If they had to go they'd go singing. The Badger made sure of that.

> 'Oh dear, Skipper, is it true
> The ship is lost and all through you?
> Bye – Bye – BASTARD.'
>> (To the tune of Bye Bye Blackbird)

They all joined in the next verse with barely concealed malice.

> 'We hope you are the first to go
> Drowned beneath the ice and snow
> Bye – Bye – BASTARD.'

The ship canted still further. Sixteen men fought the ice with axes, choppers and hammers. Anyone could see they were already too late. *Arctic Fox* was buried under 200 tons of ice increasing at an inch a minute.

A few minutes after three o'clock (everyone had now added to the creeping tension by 'clock watching') the weight of ice frozen to the superstructure alone exceeded 50 tons and the bridge leaned out over the sea. The list increased to 52 degrees. Someone cupped his hands and shouted towards the bridge, 'She'll be gone inside the hour – what game are we supposed to be playing?' The bridge couldn't hear the remark, and no one else took it up. There were no words for this. The cruel pity was that everyone knew what it would be like . . . there would be no violent lurch, with the stern reaching for the sky and the bows dipping 'goodbye'. She would lean over an inch at a time with reproachable slowness, just as she was doing now. Lean over until her fore and mizzen masts touched the water and the hull and superstructure slid resentfully beneath it. The end, when it came, would be exactly like that. Uneventful, like a human court of justice passing the death sentence.

At half past three bells rang throughout the ship, and moments later the telegraph rang and was faintly answered from the engine room. *Arctic Fox* came round and then the engine failed, leaving her athwart the sea. The foredeck was instantly flooded level with the rail and the ship went down by the head. The sea buried everything and engulfed the bridge. The propeller leapt ten feet out of the water. Suddenly the engine burst into life and the propeller plunged deep into the ocean. The ship obeyed her helm and stood head to sea.

The loudspeaker came alive with a rush of atmospherics and the Skipper spoke: 'CHOP THE GEAR! Play it smart there's not much time – we're going over.' The voice was level, only faintly commanding, and colder than anyone had the right to expect. Within twenty minutes the great trawl was axed off and left behind.

The ship was now 10 tons lighter and her resistance to wind

and waves also fell from 22,000 lb. to under a thousand. This advantage was minimised as engine power had to be increased to counter the speed loss caused by head trim, and to maintain steerage way against the wind gusting at 80 knots. The ship was steaming at 6 knots, wind ahead, and tons of spray froze while still in the air. For the remainder of that day and part of the night the crew fought to free the ship from ice. To an experienced eye she was already stricken.

If *Arctic Fox* was ever to inspire love in anyone this was her moment; perhaps the last she would have. Gone was the wide-awake look, the thrusting self-confidence, the vital buoyancy in her forepeak.

There was no love. To the twenty men she was trying to save from drowning she was just a 'bloody cow' who refused to live. A 'stubborn bitch' who wouldn't die.

CHAPTER TWELVE

The Skipper stood very still with his back straight and one foot pressed hard against the casing which skirted the apron of the bridge, the other foot held firm in the ribbing of the floor. One shoulder rested against the bulkhead and his left arm extended upwards so that his hand could find support of the brass swivel handle of the bridge top compass.

He opened the bridge window and looked down at the men fighting the ice along the length of the ship – his ship. He banged the window up but stood in the same position for a number of minutes. Then he crossed to his cabin and taking a key from his pocket unlocked the cupboard which contained the Bond. He reached inside and took out a bottle of rum, and laid it length-ways on the cabin table which had a brass gallery round its edge. Beside the bottle he put the crew's dram glass. He secured his cabin door so that it remained open and turned back on to the bridge. On the way, he leaned across into the R/T room and turned on the switch which operated the ship's loudspeaker. Then he switched it off again and turned to look at the echo sounder. He studied the double saw tooth line on the chart as it unwound, silently recording the contours of the sea-bed. From this chart it was possible to assess the width of the waves displacing the ship's keel, the lines rising and falling with the measured movement of the sea.

Arctic Fox was rolling from port to starboard at an angle of 46 degrees one way and 53 degrees the other. The Skipper picked up his private log from its table on the bridge, opened it at the first clear page and laid it flat, then he closed it and punched the cover with the ridge of his knuckles. He looked again at the deck, but could see nothing through the foam which flung a curtain of sea and spray up to the bridge windows.

Only one man stood out, and then for a fraction of a second. A man wearing a black sou'wester, with a great width of shoulder and depth of chest, swinging an axe high above his head.

The ship buried her bow and fell back, then lifted on the back of the next wave and rolled into the trough where she heeled over and leaned into the slow swell as though death had her at last in its grip. But the sea let her go, and she came up slowly from the hollow between the waves and then waited to be thrown upwards.

The Skipper watched the rev. counter swing over as the screw left the water and began to race.

Arctic Fox again fell back into a trough which nearly engulfed her. From his vantage point on the bridge, the Skipper glimpsed a wave rolling out of the darkness. A green wall of advancing water topped with a crest of white and riding as high as the foremast. A 'killer' wave.

He raced to the loudspeaker switch and turned it.

'CLEAR THE DECK!' he screamed. 'CLEAR THE DECK!'

The deck was already clear. Had the men relied on his warning they would have been lost. After a moment's pause, the Skipper spoke again to the crew who by this time had reached the safety of the door on the quarter-deck.

'Tell the Mate I want him.'

The Mate pulled off his sou'wester and made his way forward to the bridge. Meanwhile, half-frozen men groped their way to the galley. Sweat and brine had frozen on their faces, icicles had formed on eyebrows, noses and beards, and the heat of the galley fire brought acute pain to their hands and fingers.

It was Harry. He broke the shocked silence.

'We'll be bastard lucky to get away with this lot, I'll tell you. Did you feel her? Right over she was! Nearly on her fucking beam. I've been coming out this way a fair time now, haven't I, Colin, but this Skipper's mad. He'll lose this bastard ship if he doesn't turn her head to wind. I'm *telling* yer. He'll lose her, and us with 'er. We've got a 60 knot wind up our arse to start with.'

'You always were a gobbie bastard,' someone remarked.

'I'm going up to sign off.' Colin spoke with vehemence. But he wouldn't break his Articles of Agreement – some men would, but not Colin.

'Well, what *are* we going to do? Anything or owt?' a voice at the back demanded.

The opinions offered hardly did any of them credit as mariners.

'Turn north,' (why north?) 'and run aground. Beach her and then chop her clear.'

'Send a Mayday.'

'Put her on the beach wherever there's a gentle shoal.'

'The only place for a trawler in trouble is far out at sea, in deep water, with plenty of sea room.'

'Flood the bilges – she's lost her gravity.'

'Make her settle. Draw water from the condensers.'

'She's drawing more than her draught as it is. Six foot more – that's why she's not capsized already.' (An astonishingly accurate comment from the Badger.)

'Take to the boats.'

'We're in fifteen hundred foot of water!'

'240 fathom, to be exact!'

'We should call for help.'

'Start shouting then, you're good at that.'

' 'e'll *ave* to bring her round,' said Barry, 'but 'e won't to my way of thinking.'

'Why not?' shouted the crew.

'Et's joost a foony feelin' ah've got, that's all.'

'The mad bastard's *got* to.'

'Suppose we'll wait for the Mate, but it's a Board of Trade job on my reckoning.' Harry's muffled voice came from the hatch where he was looking for a pot.

'Bollocks to the Board of Trade,' said Bill, wiping condensation from the porthole and looking out. 'There's not another bastard ship up this way – not one.'

'Lave et to thar Mate,' said the Bosun, 'an' get thar cuke to make sum tay. Ah'm noot makin's ma will oot joost yet, thut's fer shure.'

'My old man,' remarked the Badger, 'told me once that fishing's a tradition – something you pass on. Well, the only thing the old bastard passed on to me was a lot of filthy language saying that fishing was a fucking awful job. He always said so, even when he was sober. He proved it, too, in the end. He died out here.'

No one answered this poignant remark.

The Skipper left the chart room, closing the door behind him. He looked down at the ladder leading from the bridge. The ladder was of varnished teak with galvanised iron treads and brass hand rails. The well at the foot of the ladder was covered with a coir mat and lit by a single bulkhead light which threw a circle of illumination on to the floor of the companionway.

The Mate stood in the circle of light. Quite still, with his hands loose at his sides and his face lifted upwards. The Skipper turned with deliberate slowness and walked quietly on to the bridge. He stood beneath the compass card in the deckhead with his left hand gripping the spoke on the summit of the ship's wheel, his right foot wedged hard against the pedestal. His face was without noticeable colour, his eyes were wide, and staring at the boiling sea. The bridge was in darkness, apart from the light in the binnacle head of the compass and glow from the rudder indicator. The wind and sea tore at the armour plate of the bridge windows and the bridge top shuddered with the force.

The Mate joined his Captain on the bridge. Frozen brine still covered his shoulders and arms, but quickly melted in the warmth. Both men turned and faced each other. The Mate had failed as a skipper – bad luck and drink had ruined his chances. He wouldn't be given any more trawlers to command. The Skipper had known his mate for sixteen years, since that first day when they sailed as deckhands together. They had accepted each other's promotion in a spirit of rivalry, and only in recent years had a feeling of reticence and caution grown between them. It wasn't jealousy. There was nothing mean or trivial about the Mate, and the Skipper didn't put on noticeable airs with anyone. He knew what the crew had been saying. The broadcast Tannoy picked up voices on the mess-deck if the key was put over on the bridge. Opinions didn't matter. He was in command, and the Mate gave the orders, not the crew. But now the row which he was certain would break over them would, on the surface at least, be a matter of conflicting opinions, leading to a choice between one of two alternatives which he would decide on. He wanted to insist that they put the gear over again and shoot away. He would argue – and the Mate was bound to agree – that the big bags came from midnight to breakfast. The swag fed head to tide in these parts – top of the gully before it ran off into deep water and rough ground. It was only a matter of running on a cable or two to bring the ship on to the new sounding. It was now 4 a.m. – time to catch the swag which would have moved away by the end of the next haul at half seven. *Then* would be the time to ease her in, bring her head round and dodge till the storm eased. He was worried about the weight of ice the ship now carried, and even more worried at the rate it was building up. But one didn't become a successful Skipper by giving way when you were still in with a chance. The Mate was bound to argue. Mates *always* argued – the Skipper had done so himself – but always without rancour, there was nothing personal in it. The

63

Skipper drove his Mate hard, used him even, but that's what mates were for. After this long silence he spoke . . .

'Get the gear over, Ken. We'll be shooting away in fifteen minutes.'

'In this weather? The Mate spoke in flat, level tones.

'Yes, why not? According to Sparks she'll blow herself out by morning.'

'How often has *he* been right lately?'

'That's not the question, is it? I'm telling you to get ready to shoot.'

'You may be interested to know one or two of the lads are likely to sign off.'

'Then I'll log 'em.'

'Think you're justified?'

'Don't you? You need all hands in this weather on the deck. And after we shoot away, call out the watch below and get to work on the ice. We'll lose her else.'

'If you admit that why risk another haul?'

'That's not for you to ask, is it?'

They argued on. Only once did they touch the personal level, when the Mate sharply retorted, 'You've lost whatever touch you had in this game and instead you're using me to carry out your bloody stupid orders'. To which the Skipper's unemotional reply was, '*Carry* them out then!'

Drama, as so often happens in real life, had ended in anti-climax.

On the mess-deck the men waited. Possibly they knew what to expect. Each man was fully rigged and lounged without noticeable relaxation with a pot of tea and a fag bent on. The Mate hurried back aft and stopped by the mess-deck door just long enough to shout his orders.

'Get the gear over. We're shooting away, bosun.'

'Raight. Joomp to et, luds!'

'Bloody suicide squad we are,' someone muttered.

Arctic Fox rolled heavily as her head came slowly round the compass. The crew, led by the Mate, came on to the deck from the half door on the starboard quarter deck. The sea was completely white and running in a confused swell. The air was filled with foam and hard driven snow, powered by a wind that blew men backwards along the deck. An Anemometer compared the speed of the gale with the speed of the ship, and after proper allowance had been made for the violent motion of the ship, recorded a sustained velocity of 64 knots! As the swell took *Arctic Fox* on the beam her stern went under and the sea roared over the boatdeck. About a dozen Mollies had been blown inboard and found it impossible to fly off the deck. At one moment gulls and men were washing about on the deck together, powerless against the fury of the sea. The winch started up and the footropes carrying the groundwire through which the massive bobbins were reeved came slowly level with the rail. No one could see, or hear the orders he was given, and after the fourth attempt to get the bobbins over the side the Mate spread his arms wide and lowered them to his sides. The bobbins crashed back into their cradle alongside the scuppers. The ship now lay right over on her beam ends. Wave after wave was sweeping clean over her. It could only be a matter of minutes now before another wave knocked her down and she rolled over, and stayed rolled over. The men exposed on the deck were in peril.

On the bridge the telephone rang. The indicator joined the handle as the engine room returned the signal to the bridge. The Sparks left the wireless room to join the Skipper, and together they forced the wheel over.

The ship started to obey the screw and her head turned slowly round the compass. Despite their efforts, she dropped back and lay starboard to leeward, with her rail submerged and her beam just showing. With the helm hard over they tried again to bring her round, but she dropped off as her screw and rudder leapt clear of the sea. The Skipper rang for increased revs, and *Arctic Fox* veered round with her head nearly into the wind. She faltered for a moment, but slowly lost headway and finally swung back out of control. The revs were again increased, but the sea thrust her back and her head refused to stay up. She was now lying at right angles to her course and drifting on the swell. The

engines gave full power and her head again came round
and then stood head to wind. With luck she would ride out the
storm.

CHAPTER THIRTEEN

The ocean, however, had not finished with her yet. A white wall
of sea water crashed down on her bridge top and stove in the
engine room skylights. A freak gust of wind corkscrewed low
across the sea and roared down the deck ventilators which now
that the ship's head had been reversed should have been turned
round. Mollies and Gannets had been flung down the ventilator
into the engine room and flapped wildly among the machinery.

The Skipper decided to stay on his present course and continue
to steam away from the centre of the storm. This, as the Mate
pointed out to the Bosun, was sheer face-saving. 'A decision's not
a decision at all when you've already rejected every bloody
alternative but one.'

As *Arctic Fox* steamed head to wind, all hands were ordered
back on the deck in an effort to clear the ice from the deck and
superstructure. The Skipper stayed at the wheel which was easier
to handle now that the telemotor was able to give greater assistance
to the rudder, but the great waves pounded on and the 10 a.m.
weather forecast was the same as for the previous day. Meanwhile,
in the R.T. room, the Sparks was trying to raise other trawlers
believed to be in range hoping to find out their weather and fishing prospects. A few British trawlers came on the air at long
intervals and then hurridly switched to another wavelength to
monitor information coming in from the Parson's Nose, a fishing
ground in the Barents Sea. A trawler as yet unidentified had been
observed on a bearing. Lat. 73° 30′ N. Long. 40° 26′ E.
She had showed up on Radar eighteen hours earlier rolling
in heavy seas with her engines stopped. As she failed to answer
the Radio Telephone a ship on the same bearing closed with
her to offer assistance. In an area of known disturbance radio

silence was not unusual, particularly if she was Russian which was thought to be the case at this time. Through night glasses she was seen to run on a cable or two and then stop. This procedure was repeated each time a sighting was made close enough to read her registration. Her line and some details of her layout confirmed that she was not Russian, but apart from that she remained a mystery. As the ship near at hand was too slow to manoeuvre at speed in heavy weather she came on the air asking for someone to take her place. A fast diesel ship offered to chase after her to see what the trouble was. It was accepted that the weather in this area was bad enough to justify laying-to without engines but no one could understand why the nameless trawler should keep edging away from the ship offering assistance. The fast diesel struck heavy going and received damage from pack ice ahead. Rather than change course the diesel edged her way through at slow ahead, entering the area on the morning of the second day following the first sighting of the mystery ship. Coming up fast on her port quarter, the diesel called her by radio. She refused to reply and turned away on a course which would bring her up on the Russian coast if she persisted in it. The diesel was reluctant to head her off, as this would take her inside the Russian limit. The diesel reported back, gave her position and decided to lie in wait. The engineers, meanwhile, repaired the telemotor and a broken feed valve. With pack ice closing round her and a heavy coating building up on her decks she was about to turn away when the mystery ship showed up on Radar steaming north along the coast. The diesel laid a course to intercept and got underway. The mystery ship stood on her course for another ten miles and then hauled round in a circle and came on at full speed straight for the diesel. The diesel turned her deck lights on and trained her searchlights for'ard over her bows. Tension was evident among the ships near enough to know what was going on, and the word 'mutiny' came crackling over the air.

On board *Arctic Fox* the fight to save the ship went on with every man nearing the limit of his endurance. After twelve hours it was decided to call a ten-minute halt and over a dram of rum the Bosun was asked to guess the nationality of the mystery ship. Sparks had made a sketch based on details relayed back from trawlers in the area. He laid it on the mess-deck table, and the Bosun shaded his eyes to study it. An outstanding feature was a new canvas dodger made to provide shelter aft of the winch and secured to the bridge apron with well rigged guy lines. Deckmen occasionally rig up a square of odd canvas over the winch platform to keep the weather out, but such things are not standard equipment and none are supplied ready made up. The dodger on the mystery ship fitted perfectly and had in addition drop sides and a metal hood, or loudspeaker cone, extending out over the port winch drum. The foremast platform mounted three searchlights instead of the usual one, and both derricks were secure inboard. No trawler swings her derricks in until after she turns for home. Nothing more was known of her layout, but from the sketch made of her outline the Bosun pronounced her British. Her characteristic bridge and the disposition of her electrical gear on the bridge top gave her away.

This startling pronouncement was relayed back to the fast diesel moving through the black night in shocking visibility, looking for the trawler steaming towards her a mile ahead. Suddenly she stopped and went astern. Within four minutes she was underway once more, this time back the way she had come. The diesel reached the position where the mystery ship had stopped and found a Dan (buoy) which she hooked aboard without stopping. The Dan was of a pattern supplied to British trawlers – except for the Radar reflector which was well made, highly polished and made to rotate. The floats were dry on the upper side and the pole was dry above the water line. The Dan had been in the sea a matter of minutes. The trawler was an estimated 26 seconds ahead, but as the diesel increased speed to overhaul her she vanished completely. The scanner showed the area clear for 20 miles. At this point the diesel stopped and a conference was held to decide what to do. The fuel she had already used up would restrict her freedom later on, and with the weather hardening all the time the diesel Skipper decided to search a limited area only and, if unsuccessful, to abandon the chase. A look-out was kept for wreckage, and the latest information relayed back to the other trawlers.

Meanwhile, *Arctic Fox's* plight – unknown before the Sparks went on the air to ask about the weather – was causing concern amongst the ships near enough to give assistance (the nearest was 61 miles away) and was the subject of much critical comment from experienced Skippers who raved and cursed over the air all at once and often in strident tones too loud to be intelligible. Here, they said, was another classic example of a ship putting herself in trouble for the sake of another haul which had not paid off and left her in danger of turning over. Their candour was brutal – particularly, one must assume, to *Arctic Fox's* Skipper standing silently on the bridge of his stricken ship listening through the atmospherics to the abuse being hurled at him from all points of the compass.

Skippers are frankly disloyal, and lack even the semblance of unity or goodwill. This attitude changes only when a ship is in trouble. Then – and only then – could a bond be considered to exist. Even then it is made clear in subtle, indefinable ways, that the bond exists for the ship – more particularly the crew – and not the Captain. The Captain becomes a convenient repository for all mistakes and miscalculations; carries the burden of their conscience. If the Skipper is successful or personally disliked, rancour can be expected. Ashore and alone, Skippers will admit to being fallible, confess their greed, acknowledge – indirectly – their dread of failure. These are inherent in the fiercely competitive atmosphere of fishing. At sea these passed – like poaching inside the limit – without comment, until someone was caught out. Then for once Skippers were united, but against the culprit. It was regrettable to find men who shared a common hazard so consumed with rancour, particularly as mariners are in the popular view brave men, presupposing loyalty in misfortune – a quality more becoming than the barracking and catcalls now crackling over the air. *Arctic Fox's* Skipper could, of course, answer back – give as good as he got. Tell them to mind their own business. But nothing stood to be gained. Defeat, we know, is an orphan, and by the same reckoning failure is an orphan, too. Against good advice the Skipper had made a mistake – possibly a serious mistake – and clumsy handling by the Sparks had made the matter public knowledge.

The Skipper took the sensible course. He left the bridge, collected some deck gear from his cabin and went down on the deck to help axe away the ice.

The mystery trawler had reappeared on the Radar scanner of the diesel. Looking somewhat longer than a conventional trawler and steaming on a parallel course towards the diesel. The diesel eased in, turned round and positioned herself so as to be able to come alongside and make a close inspection. As the range closed, it was apparent the mystery ship was coming on very fast, and the diesel – already underway half a mile ahead – began to doubt if she could keep up with her long enough to make a positive identification. Then the blob on the Radar was seen to lose way and turn at right angles to her course, at which point she stopped with her larboard beam against the swell. The diesel turned without easing in and rang on full ahead. This time she was certain to overhaul her quarry. With heaving lines ready and a full crew on deck she came alongside and stopped. Her 'quarry' was a Russian gunboat! Angry, but impressed, the Skipper went astern with the Russians on the bridge waving him away and shouting what was interpreted as abuse over the loudspeaker. Running astern a cable or two, the diesel narrowly avoided a submarine of great length. In taking avoiding action her stern came round fast, narrowly missing a second submarine whose Klaxon blared incessantly. The Radar showed the diesel some distance outside the limit, but a hurried check of her charts revealed that she was, in fact, the wrong side of the line by half a mile. The scanner was now alive with ships converging on a central point in the pivot of which stood the diesel. The best course was to beat it back to friendly waters as fast as possible. The gunboat would doubtless follow, but was not considered likely to make an arrest as the disposition of the gear on board the diesel clearly indicated that she was not fishing or likely to do so.

A snow blizzard was now raging, making it impossible to pick out ships on the Radar and the searchlights had to be turned off to improve visibility from the bridge. There was speculation among the waiting ships as to whether another trawler should be sent to escort the diesel out from what was now revealed as the centre of the Russian Navy at exercise. Of the mystery ship there was no sign, and opinion was divided between those who thought she'd gone down and those who believed she was either inviting trouble for reasons of her own or otherwise engaged in some sort of mission. The latter view was favoured by those who thought the 'cones' or 'hoods' were, in fact, movie cameras loaded with film sensitive enough to take pictures in the dark. This surmise was discounted by others who thought it most unlikely that the trawler's owners would countenance a 'mission' which prevented one of their ships fishing for days on end and left her open to arrest for being inside the limit of another country's shoreline. The majority agreed, however, that trawlers did occasionally indulge in espionage in the Barents Sea, with British naval officers signed on as 'pleasure trippers'. One Aberdeen Skipper claimed to have helped load tele-photo lenses aboard, along with equipment cased in weather-proof canvas stamped 'RN'. The mystery looked like remaining unsolved, however, as the diesel turned away in a blinding snowstorm.

Many tense hours lay ahead as she made her way back to a more secure station – her course littered with half submerged submarines, the occasional ice-breaker, and with the gunboat's searchlights flooding her boat-deck. Away from the confusion, and working in the cool climate of his critical senses, a trawler Skipper (a master mariner with long service in the Navy) tried to piece the facts together. His only certain conclusion was that the mystery trawler was British. She was under the effective command of her captain. The gunboat's flag signal 'U' (You are standing into danger) meant what it said and had no sinister connotation. The mystery trawler was keeping close station with at least one underwater vessel for a purpose not known; she carried equipment designed for a purpose unconnected with trawling. That, for the present, was all anyone knew for certain.

The focus of attention was now directed towards *Arctic Fox*.

This time it was constructive and helpful. *Arctic Fox's* Sparks had adopted the 'turn the other cheek' attitude, and was being frank but diplomatic in accordance with the known wishes of the Skipper who was levering ice off the boat deck with a crowbar. What degree of list had *Arctic Fox* got? Had anyone tried using Glycol? Steam hoses? Was there an oxy-acetylene torch aboard? Why not run for shelter? How bad was the icing-up? One vessel had already altered course to intercept, announcing to everyone except *Arctic Fox* that she was providing escort. This vessel's altruism was immediately suspect, as she was constantly on the look-out for hovels which carry great prize money, as does 'stand-by' which she was now seeking. She turned back soon after and was the subject of sharp exchange over the air from skippers who had rightly guessed her motives. (The Skipper was the Badger's brother.)

Meanwhile, *Arctic Fox*, with her head up before the storm, had run into the currents of the Great Trans Polar Drift. Ice floes, riding fast, ground and rode up against each other, kicking against the hull with enough force to dislodge spanners secured to hooks in the engine room. The cook lost most of the remaining usable china and the galley boy suffered concussion and minor burns. With the sum of *Arctic Fox's* ills steadily mounting, the Skipper dropped down from the boat deck and signalled the Mate to follow him on to the bridge. Once in his cabin the Skipper ignored the losing battle being fought with the ice and stayed silent about the offers of assistance which he now knew had been made by the other ships. Two, at least, had decided to close with *Arctic Fox* and keep station with her as a matter of prudence. Others were in urgent radio communication, and generally showed more concern than *Arctic Fox's* seemingly indifferent Skipper.

The ship had not, the Skipper considered, been catching fish because the trawl was wrong. The twenty-five fathom bridles were to be replaced by ones of thirty fathoms. The headline was to be measured with a two-foot stick and lengthened or shortened accordingly. New bobbins were to be reeved on the ground wire because one was waterlogged and another was cracked. The square which had been hurriedly laced up last haul was to be mended by shooting in spare net. The door on the port side was to be keel hauled and shackled up to the starboard gallows. Finally, the headline, foot-rope and quarter rope were to be parted from the butterfly and the bracket assembly replaced by a new one.

It is not unusual for Skippers faced with slack fishing to re-rig the gear, or even to order the entire trawl to be made up on the other side of the ship; tow port instead of starboard. Failure to catch fish is put down to some inscrutable circumstance with human error and miscalculation as purely marginal factors. Changing the gear serves as a new incantation. If the fish cannot be charmed into the trawl by this method, a more potent formula has to be thought up. The fact that altering the gear does occasionally result in fishing picking up can often be accounted for by the simple expedient of having steamed on to new ground at a favourable moment – one that coincides with the completion of alterations to the gear and the fish being present on a particular shoal sounding at just that moment. Good judgement and local knowledge are not reckoned as having brought about this change of fortune, but are in some obscure way believed to have militated against its earlier fulfilment! Thus with common sense at a premium, it is thought best to utter some weird incantation – 'Change the trawl!' – rather than follow a course of action based on logic. You cannot be proved wrong if you suffer defeat at the hands of some mysterious Providence which is, in the last analysis, both accountable and beyond the orbit of man's control. It is said that skippers first become aware of the powers of this mystique on the day they take over their first command, and that it appears at its most irresistible when things are going wrong (due, presumably, to some purely human piece of folly). It follows that less susceptible beings – mates, for instance – are not open to the powers which this mystique confers and by the same token are unlikely to understand its devious workings. This is seen as a good reason for not telling mates too much of what's going on in case they dash off and do something which turns out to be right.

Against this kind of reasoning (fortified on this occasion by a wand made of wood and silver paper by the obedient Sparks), the Mate was bound to be at a disadvantage, particularly as he was trying on purely logical grounds to spare his exhausted crew hours of endless labour. He knew from bitter past experience that the rules of argument, ostensibly simple, would quickly become obscure and difficult to follow, ending with the Skipper using his authority to impose a decision – 'seeing as we fail to agree and someone must decide if we're going to pull out and make a trip'. The Mate had, on this occasion, one ace of somewhat doubtful value, and that was the inability of the deckmen to stand up any longer without sleep and the hazard to the ship if they were eventually taken off ice-breaking to work on the trawl. The trawl, he reasoned, could wait. The ice couldn't. Or if it was relegated into a second priority position it would build up and even if the ship didn't keel over the list would leave the deck raked at such an angle as to make work impossible; even if frostbite didn't strike first, or death by drowning finish them all. He didn't understand how someone who had himself been a deckman and later a mate could be so ruthless as to give orders which were reckless and unnecessary. It was useless, anyway, to change bridles until it was known where they were going or if they could get there. There was time enough for that when the ship came up on the new ground, the depth of water ascertained and the new sounding selected. We cannot, the Mate concluded, steam about the ocean in an unseaworthy ship playing a game which amounted to nothing more than water divining. Apart from retorting, with some justice, that 'water divining' was criticised only when it failed, the Skipper dropped the subject. After a moment, he spoke again.

'Last haul there were plenty of fish markings on the sounder, yet when we hauled the fish hardly covered the pounds. About five baskets on my reckoning.'

'The fish had already taken off,' said the Mate.

'How can you know that?'

'You'll catch 'em running with the tide, not when you're towing against it.'

'That change of sounding should have brought us on 'em.'

74

'It did, but you didn't have enough towing revs.'

'The reason we lost 'em was the fault of the trawl – the head-line's short by half a fathom and that fore-door's had the bracket welded back in the wrong place.'

The Mate looked a little sad, as if he'd heard this kind of complaint before.

'We can't chop an' change the gear in this weather and you know it. The ice comes first.'

'It'll take time.'

'Time *has* not and *will* not alter that. We must get away from here. Away from the weather. Give ourselves a chance – before it's too late.'

'You never spoke like that when you had a ship.'

'I never had to. I never went looking for trouble.'

'You think I am, then?'

'You know damn well it was evens whether you got her head to sea last time – before she went straight to the bottom. Less pressure in the boilers and you wouldn't have got her laid at all. She would have foundered.'

'We've seven days to get a trip in. I'm not spending it bringing her round every time it blows. My old man wouldn't have.'

'Your old man did most of his fishing four miles off Flamborough Head – within pissing distance of the lighthouse. You couldn't get him away from it – not even in the summer!'

'He fished off Iceland eight years!'

'Ay, not as Skipper he didn't.'

'Maybe.'

'Maybe's right.'

'I want that fore-door swapped over.'

'You're not getting it.'

'The bobbins?'

'Ay, when she fines away.'

'And the trawl?'

'There's nothing wrong with the trawl. It stays the way it is. An' if you want some advice, it's this – get out of this pack ice and lay a course back to the other ships. That way you'll get a trip in and still be around to spend the money!'

'Mind you don't get the pedlar's pack. I'd hate to deal the last card!'

'Who to? Yourself?'

'Watch it – that's all.'

'I'll do that.'

The Skipper stood up from the seat-locker and made for the R/T room, holding the door for the Mate making ready to go back on the deck.

CHAPTER FOURTEEN

Arctic Fox was free from imminent capsize after 21 hours, the deckmen having worked 'all hands' followed by normal watch below. With the work completed, the crew crouched close together in a single file, with heads down. On the seventh wave they moved fast together along the quarter-deck and then followed each other through the aft door – to safety. At almost the same time *Arctic Fox* ran free of the pack ice and on into clear water. This change of fortune was followed by the Radar coming back into use, and later by *Arctic Fox* closing with the rest of the 'fleet' – taking station alongside her sister ship who had eased in to wait for her. Together, in convoy, they steamed due east at 12 knots following reports of good fishing. These reports coincided with the gale fining away, but the sea still heaved and boiled with great savagery. Each new wave threw the ships back, and those without an auto-pilot needed two men at the helm to hold the course. Before long news of what was now confirmed as a 'fish shop' had reached other ships who were beating their way across the Arctic Sea as fast as they could go. Trawlers from Russia, Norway, Germany and Iceland showed up on Radar. The Russians led the race in their fast diesels, many with re-inforced bows raked to cut through ice. At the rear were the coal-burners, black smoke pouring from their stacks in an effort to keep up.

Well behind the rest was an old coal-burner from Aberdeen skippered by a villainous-looking Scot whose demeanour was of a piece with his appearance. His inquisitive ears, united with long experience of deep-water fishing, usually found him in the lead when fish were about. This report had – presumably – caught him unawares, but his crew was already out on the deck fussing over the trawl and preparing the Dan Buoy. Once on the fishing grounds he would steam at full speed to the centre, launch his buoy and tow by hauling round in a circle – a method designed to keep everyone else out. On this occasion, however, he would be too late, being already ten hours behind everyone else. On *Arctic Fox's* bridge his rasping voice came over the Tannoy, relating its tale of woe.

On first receiving the report the Aberdeen Skipper (known to everyone as 'Mac the Bastard') was bobbing off in his cabin with his feet resting on the open drawer of his seat-locker. As he jumped up the ship rolled to port trapping both feet in the drawer. He hobbled on to the bridge in a vicious mood and started to abuse the helmsman. The helmsman said something which didn't amuse Mac the Bastard, who threw him forcibly off the bridge. He then flung the wheel over, turning the ship at a 45 degree angle to her course. This abrupt alteration knocked both the firemen unconscious and flung the coal from the bunkers. Ignoring the engine room whistle, Mac the Bastard laid a course and brought his ship round on a bearing ready to set off in pursuit. Having rung on full ahead, he limped off the bridge to get some elastoplast without noticing the ship was slowly losing way. The voice pipe over his bunk was unstoppered so he didn't hear the engine room whistle there either. From the cabin he crossed back onto the bridge, past the unattended wheel and into the radio room to do some eavesdropping. Meanwhile, his ship zig-zagged along at 3 knots, slowly dropping off until it was pointing away from its course altogether. With his ear clamped against the loudspeaker, Mac the Bastard listened with mounting excitement as the magic words, '100 baskets – 2 bags' were repeated time and again. On wet steam and at her best speed of 10 knots, Mac the Bastard reckoned his ship was well placed for her share. Once in the area he would frighten everyone away by bearing down on them – sounding off here and there – and drop his marker on the fish shop. No advantage in being shy, polite even. No one was ever polite to Mac the Bastard so they were only getting back what they dished out. His intentions were clear enough. Whatever they were, they puzzled the two men left on watch. Looking out they noticed their ship galloping all over the place until finally it stopped altogether. Thinking their Skipper might be on the bottle they agreed to make their way to the bridge and find out. By the time they reached it the ship was underway again at a speed of 6 knots. Their first duty was to check the course chalked up on the blackboard. Having done this they put the wheel over to bring the ship on to the bearing and settled down to wait for the return of the helmsman. For the next hour they took turns at the wheel, bringing the ship's head dutifully round each time it fell off. They were, presumably, feeling quite pleased with themselves because when the Skipper appeared they told him with pride what they had done.

In telling this story over the air, Mac the Bastard nearly choked when he came to this bit, and no one knew for certain what happened to the two watch-men (The Badger, who had sailed under Mac the Bastard said they'd most likely been eaten by this time.) Eventually the ship came round on the correct course and galloped along behind the others. But almost at once she lost way and stopped. The bridge door slid back on its runners and the chief engineer came on to the bridge. He told how the two firemen had been knocked out and added that he had taken ten minutes to struggle free of the coal which fell on top of him. Mac dismissed this as trivial, adding that engineers were always complaining of something. Why, he asked, had the ship stopped? She had stopped, the Chief explained, because the firemen were too stunned to stoke the fires. Mac pushed past him and made for the engine room. There, wearing his Balaclava helmet, bicycle clips and bottle opener round his neck, he shovelled away furiously for an hour or more. By the time he sat down to rest, steam was squeaking from joints, oil smoking on pistons and cams and the pressure gauges were above danger level. Having set an example for others to follow, Mac went back to the bridge. In the chart room he decided to plot a new course, which he chalked on the blackboard before going back to the wireless room to carry on eavesdropping. The ship was equipped with an ordinary card compass, adjusted to the magnetic meridian. This required new calculations to be made at every change of course to allow for deviation in a ship built almost entirely of iron and designed to work in an area of known disturbance. Either the compass adjusters ashore had compensated too much or too little or Mac had chalked up the wrong course. Whatever the reason, Mac's ship bounced along at 10 knots making for the southern-most point of Greenland. When another ship noticed him on Radar going away from the others, she came up on the air asking if Mac the Bastard had found a fish shop of his own. Mac was baffled by this remark, but he chuckled – just in case it was meant to be funny. No, he replied, his bearing was based on course, speed and distance calculated to bring him up with the rest in no time. A shorter route, he added pleasantly. When his listener observed that the shortest route was also the shortest distance, Mac wondered what sort of fool he was dealing with. What I mean is, said the voice, why are you going via Cape Farewell? Mac turned the Tannoy off in disgust and strolled on to the bridge to look at *his* Radar. And there he was – bustling along miles from anywhere and quite alone. He hauled round once again and set off in pursuit. Then he was on the air every twenty minutes asking everyone in turn how the fishing was going. All gave the same reply. This ship was filling her boots, that ship was choked with fish. Some were laid to give the deckmen time to empty the pounds before shooting away. Faced with this news Mac switched the Tannoy off and kept radio silence for the rest of the day.

Actually, none of the trawlers had yet reached the new fishing ground. It was some hours before the leading ship reported she was there, and shortly afterwards *Arctic Fox* herself came on to the ground, scrutinised through powerful glasses.

Because of inadequate charts navigators were once carried on trips to this area, as the number of 'fastenings' still unmarked or found to have moved from their known locations were still considerable. There are 57 charted wrecks around Bear Island alone and a number yet to be discovered, as this area was on the line of route for the wartime convoys to Russia. The latest King-fisher charts are as accurate as any now available, and depend on trawler skippers for information about new 'fastenings' or movement of known wrecks. Some of these had probably come to rest in the gullies and been flattened by the enormous weight of the sea to which they had been subject for a quarter of a century. Others, however, would have gone down on to the relatively flat rock bed with their superstructure still more or less intact. The merchantmen with their welded hulls would have broken up or been blasted to pieces, and it was from these that the greatest damage or loss was likely to occur. Turning slowly in the pale green water they clang their way along the clean black rock, sounding an endless death knell from their final resting place – with the decayed bones of their gallant crews still trapped in the twisted metal or turning endlessly in the water-filled bulkheads below decks. It is some consolation to know that they are not forgotten. Among trawlermen, young and old alike, being in this area engenders a feeling which comes as near to compassion as most of them are likely or able to get. A typical comment delivered in a deceptively matter-of-fact way was made by Rubber Nose when passing over the wreck of the 'Hood' during an earlier fishing trip off Iceland. 'Just think of those poor bastards down there.' Such introspection is received in silence more telling than the intoning of prayers or casting of wreaths.

Arctic Fox began to position herself. The Skipper rang for 'Half Ahead' and almost at once the ship's bow went under as her speed dropped. She ran on five cable lengths before turning on to the sounding where she stopped. Searchlights came on and soon the ship was ablaze with light along her entire weather side. The Dan Buoy was launched over the port rail, followed by the grapnel. The Skipper gave the final helm order before attention was transferred to the Mate bracing himself against the rail alongside the fore-pound.

'Cod End outboard! LET GO!!'

Within eight minutes the most vital operation carried out on a trawler at sea had been completed, but unfortunately the trawl was partly paralysed. In putting the gear over the side the can line fouled an obstruction five fathoms below the surface. It was necessary to haul in and free the obstruction before shooting away again. As the trawl broke the surface a length of copper wire came up with it. This was arrested with the aid of a short-haul while Harry and Buster took up the slack which they flaked out along the deck. They hauled up fifty feet of the wire, and after freeing the end from the trawl found a copper buoy fastened to it.

CHAPTER FIFTEEN

The headline broke the surface, and with it came a German sea-mine. The Skipper jumped to the wheel to put the helm over and carry the net clear of the ship's side. Engines were shut off with only the lighting dynamo kept running. Other trawlers were warned off over the R/T and the net was dragged inboard hand over hand. The two off-duty engineers lined the rail looking down at the trawl now partly floating like some giant sea anemone.

The mine rolled lazily on the swell and with slow, Teutonic thoroughness closed with the hull plates of the ship. The cry went up 'FENDERS. FETCH SOME FENDERS'. On the bridge the Skipper flung the wheel hard over and waited for signs of movement. The gap slowly widened as the trawl ran back over the rail, taking the mine with it. Suddenly the cross wind took the ship's head off and she drifted back. 'WHERE'S THE BLOODY FENDERS?' roared the Mate, pushing the mine away with a boat hook thrust through the open scupper port. The fenders arrived as the mine scraped the hull plates, leaving a scar along the ship's side. On the bridge the Skipper unstoppered the voice pipe and called the engine room. 'Chief? You'd best come up. We're in trouble. Play it smart.'

The mine had waited a long time for this moment. It had waited a long time to confirm its patriotism and shorten the war. It rose on the swell until it was level with the ship's rail. Its buoy ring struck hard, and the mine rolled over and over along the ship's side with a sound that will remain for ever. Seeping out from it, with a fresh and vivid significance, was a widening trail of white fluid. 'HACKSAWS!' yelled the Skipper from the bridge. 'HACK IT CLEAR OF THE NET.'

It was impossible to control the swing away from the mine, and it closed again with a loud, metallic clang. That clang stopped every man dead in his tracks. Hacksaws were brought, and the Mate was lowered over the side with Harry and Buster gripping his ankles.

It took an hour to free the mine from the trawl. It was the longest hour anyone could remember. The copper line lashed about the deck with enough force to cut a man in two before it finally whipped over the side and disappeared into the sea. The mine floated alongside the ship for a number of minutes until caught by the current and carried astern. *Arctic Fox* started her engines and completed a wide sheer before easing in. The mine tumbled in the wake, symbolising the lasting reach of war. Finally, it sank back into the deep ocean.

Arctic Fox suffered further delay whilst the gear was brought back inboard for the trawl to be inspected. The Mate showed signs of ill temper at this point, as he sensed (correctly as it turned out) that he would be blamed for the delay in shooting away. This may sound unreasonable, as it was obvious he could have known nothing of the mine and had not chosen the sounding. The Skipper had chosen the sounding. But getting the gear away is entirely the Mate's responsibility and in this matter there are no shades of black and white. If successful, the operation passes without comment. If not, the Mate would get a bollocking from the bridge – justified or not.

On this occasion the bollocking was more savage than the circumstances called for and lasted on and off for all of ten minutes. It was the Mate who had suggested they joined the other ships, and indirectly he was responsible for catching the mine. The Mate in turn cursed the Bosun who made unpleasant noises to the deckies – who as usual took no notice whatsoever. There's an old saying among deckies – the Skipper's never wrong, the Mate's seldom wrong and the Bosun's sometimes wrong. But the deckies are *always* wrong.

Having lost two hours' fishing time the trawl was successfully shot away at five o'clock in the morning – commencing a tow across ten miles of ocean, littered with a greater concentration of wrecks per square mile than any other and also – everyone hoped – an equally great concentration of fish. One must follow the fish, but clearly the ground was not suitable for trawling and someone in the tight-knit group would lose his gear before long. Towing in complete darkness and without an horizon requires each trawler's movements to remain predictable to the others. Abrupt changes of course – as happens at hauling time – must be anticipated rather than be seen after the manoeuvre is under way. Radar is the only method of doing this and is a very imperfect instrument when compared with the human eye. This hazard is not improved by the stubborn refusal of ships keeping close station to give way to each other. The Russians and Germans are implacable in this respect, but among ships sharing a common language the hazard is understandably less acute. Most British trawlers are careful not to foul another ship's gear (Mac the Bastard being an exception), and the Russians are particularly painstaking in retrieving their own nets and those of other ships – releasing them as quickly as possible and with a minimum of damage. They also maintain a number of efficient ice-breakers which would come to the aid of any ship in urgent need of assistance. Calls from the Germans, however, are seldom answered. The Germans have an unpleasant reputation on the deep water grounds, particularly for their handling of any fishing gear which might come into their possession. Their best known method for dealing with this is to burn it off with torches and throw it into the sea. A complete trawl floating free on the surface, and in darkness, is always a great worry as it either fouls propellers or paralyses gear. One British skipper who lost his gear to the Germans closed with the offender who hurriedly dumped the severed trawl right on to the ship's screw, crippling the ship which then had to be towed 200 miles to land. The trawler was laid up for five days, made a loss for her owners — who in turn made the skipper pay for the lost trawl.

Arctic Fox had herself clashed with a German on the trip before this one, when the German ignored the towing lights showing on the mast head and cut across her outlying gear with the object of seeing how much fish lay in the pounds. *Arctic Fox* drove her off by firing a large box of coloured signal rockets which were on board ready for dumping in deep water. Each direct hit was loudly cheered and one penetrated the German's bridge, forcing the occupants out on to the verandah where they were pelted with rubbish and loudly booed. Neither side showed much common sense on this occasion, but the German was at fault for ignoring collision regulations. She would not have taken such a liberty with the Russians, and would have been well advised had she avoided trouble in an area where past actions are still remembered with particular bitterness.

Iceland is also hostile to British trawler crews, who are regarded as drunkards and troublemakers. Their unfriendliness is presumed to have its origins in the last war when some troops made an unfavourable impression. Often, it is believed, the Germans would have been more welcome as an occupying force, and they are noticeably more welcome today than the British. They speak, in many instances, a common language, and their relationship has not been embittered by the recent 'gunboat war' which the Icelanders were obliged to call off. Negotiations have been going on in recent months to bring about some measure of agreement between United Kingdom trawler owners and the Icelandic Government. They are generally expected to reach an agreement based on expediency and compromise, which will remain partially effective if Britain joins the Common Market. Or otherwise honoured in particular instances where one side enjoys an advantage based on vested interests. If the advantage is later seen to have been overtaken by the concession given to secure it, some 'incident' at sea will readily serve as sufficient reason to break the agreement and bring back the gunboats 'to restore order'. This view may sound unnecessarily cynical – it is, nevertheless, held by numbers of deep-water skippers who know the Icelanders and also the trawler owners. Among skippers who know something of the private opinions of the negotiators on both sides is held the view that no cynicism of theirs could match that of the parties involved.

CHAPTER SIXTEEN

The first ship to shoot away on the new ground was ready to haul at 6 a.m. Upwards of a dozen skippers lowered their bridge windows to train night glasses on the trawl the moment it broke the surface. *Arctic Fox's* Bosun was called to the bridge where his commentary was listened to with interest. The ship had her washer reversed after only six days' fishing, indicating that her fish room was already half full. The shoot had been rigged to serve the fore hatch below, while the staging would have been made up ready to deliver fish for shelving in the remaining pounds. Jealousy was hard to conceal – she was a Yorkie, too. She hauled just one fish – a very small fish at that. There was only one short burst of laughter on *Arctic Fox's* bridge, and that was caused by nerves, not satisfaction. Someone, it appeared, had taken everyone else for a ride. There was nothing left to do but continue towing and watch to see what the others caught.

The next ship to haul reported her catch hardly covered the deck of the pounds, and the third ship lost her complete trawl.

The hunt was now on to find the practical joker, but in fact he was never found. Suspicion fell on Mac the Bastard, but he was cleared when someone reported him still chasing after the others. The Russians were the first to give up. Maintaining radio silence they turned away east, led by their factory ship and attended by the never absent gunboat. The Germans finished their unrewarding tow and then they, too, broke away and made off in all directions. With so many trawlers turning off the ground, *Arctic Fox* abandoned her tow and stood off a mile from the rest. Clearly she was again in trouble, this time for a different reason. As expected, the Skipper ordered the Bosun (the Mate had gone on watch below) to overhaul the trawl and unshackle the bridles. This was carried out in an atmosphere of silent bad temper, with the Bosun having fits of rage and confusing everyone. Shortly after breakfast *Arctic Fox* turned and got underway, following her previous course which, if maintained, would take her back into the storm. The nine o'clock dram of rum improved tempers a little but an air of gloom and fatalism was spreading everywhere.

Meanwhile, Mac the Bastard had quickly sensed there was no fish where he was going and had wasted no time in hauling round to intercept *Arctic Fox*! Anything Mac did was viewed with suspicion, particularly as he shunned company and told no one what he was up to. Aggressive, sarcastic and self-satisfied, he was nevertheless capable and had an enviable success record as a top skipper; a fact endorsed by his crew, who loved and hated him – convinced he was mad, but wouldn't think of sailing under anyone else. When he came alongside later in the day, he used his helm and engines to close with *Arctic Fox* so that he would be near enough to shout across. His cook, he said, 'was short of tinned milk' and 'would *Arctic Fox* float some over?' 'Please,' he added, as an afterthought.

The sea was so heavy that his canary-coloured trawler towered high above *Arctic Fox* on the swell, before it fell into the trough and disappeared from view. Synchronising his engines with *Arctic Fox's*, he kept his ship's head up and maintained distance with customary skill. Having got his milk inboard (no question of an exchange) he went quickly astern and steamed off into the night. This little episode was all of a piece with Mac's method of conducting business. By carefully avoiding any use of the radio he had not given his position away or let himself in for one of those pseudo-pleasant two-way chats the subtleties of which left him at a disadvantage.

Arctic Fox's fish room tally showed 750 kit, with six days' fishing left. To make a trip she would need at least two thousand kit, with as many large sprags as possible. Having just lost a further nine hours (equivalent to three hauls) luck was needed if the situation was to be saved. The Skipper needed luck, but of more importance he needed some idea of what to do next. He was considerably distressed by news of the good fortune of practically everyone he spoke to over the air.

All had done well, due mainly to their keeping together and remaining in contact with one another. Each admitted it had been a long, hard slog with a lot of mending in between, but it was quite plain that the firm's other ships, operating in reasonable weather and on well-tried ground, had pulled out. It was against his temperament to join them – now or at any other time, and he was disliked enough not to be asked. It is in moments like these when luck is running out that the essential loneliness of a skipper's job at sea is most apparent. The noticeably undemocratic life on a trawler plays a large part in this. Every skipper understands the peculiar psychology of his deck-hands and the difficulties facing his officers in carrying out unpopular orders. Yet few accept advice in decision making. It is not unusual for crews, including mates, to remain in ignorance of what is required of them until the last moment. No one would think of asking a skipper what his next move was likely to be, or feel free to discuss it with him once he had been told. A skipper's most likely confidant is his radio officer – the most hated man on a trawler, and the least talkative. Skippers in turn express great bitterness when their decisions are criticised – failing to understand why their crew should resent orders calculated to benefit them. Thus, when things are going badly and tempers already frayed, master and men reach the perfect impasse. Such an impasse certainly existed aboard *Arctic Fox* at this time.

CHAPTER SEVENTEEN

Currently, the Skipper refused to talk to the Mate, and gave his orders through the Bosun. The Bosun passed on half the orders, leaving out those likely to enrage his senior. The Mate in turn declined to take instructions from the Bosun and issued orders of his own. These orders were countermanded by the Skipper from the bridge as soon as the deckmen started acting upon them. The Mate instantly reversed the countermand from the bridge, and ordered the Bosun to ask the Skipper not to interfere with work on the deck. The Skipper refused the request and gave the Bosun orders independent of the Mate. The Mate obstructed the few orders the Bosun attempted to carry out and finally instructed him off the deck altogether. The Bosun refused to go and began working aft with two deckies (Badger and Whippit), renewing the messenger hook which the Mate's deckies had themselves just renewed. By this time the crew were divided into three. Those who for reasons of self-interest stuck to the Mate; others, wary of the Mate and also fearful of the Skipper, stood apart and did nothing. And finally, the Bosun's two deckmen – who were simply obeying the last order (which in their case was not, in fact, the last order they were given, but the one most acceptable to them personally). At one moment, the deckmen port side were hoisting net from the forehold while deckmen starboard side were stowing it in the net bins under the whaleback. The Bosun's two men pulled the net out and on to the foredeck, whereupon the Mate's helpers lowered it back down the forehold. The for'ard gilson was used for the lifting and lowering, but two different wiremen operated the winch barrel as one had been ordered to raise the net from the hold and *not* to lower it and the other had been told to lower it and not to *raise* it. Never could such a tragicomedy have been played out against such a bizarre setting – searchlights, snow, ice, sleet, drift-ice, screaming winds and mountainous seas.

During this time *Arctic Fox* stood on a course which took her west of Bear Island which she passed at a distance of 3 miles at a speed of 10 knots – giving her 6 minutes to cover a nautical mile. There was no horizon and visibility, without the foremast searchlight, was less than a cable. All bridge lights were off to aid sighting and the ship was less than 16 degrees off her set course. There was no helmsman on the bridge, as the crew were still playing musical chairs down on the deck. The fact was that *Arctic Fox* had been steaming through drift-ice for four and a half minutes before she struck the edge of the pack-ice where her stem rose clear of the water and she ground to a stop. She came to rest with one third of her length tilted upwards, buried in a glacier-carved valley the lower end of which was inundated by the sea. With a draught of 16 ft. 0 in., and 60 ft. 0 in. of her keel clear of the water the angle at which she now stood can easily be imagined. This, as it turned out, was the one thing that saved her. Buoyed by the sea lifting her stern, she inched her way slowly back into the water. Once her stern had slid far enough down the wall of ice, her engines racing astern pulled her clear. This was the nearest she had yet come to total destruction, and the damage was less than might have been expected. She had an impressive dent in her bow plates and her stem had been arched back by the impact. One unfortunate consequence of the collision was that the leak in the chain locker previously pumped dry by the engineers would again need ceaseless attention.

In the galley All Sorts saved himself from serious scalding by swinging to and fro on the pipes running topside of the galley bulkhead. Unfortunately, he lost his grip and fell bottom first into a large cheese and potato pie made ready for dinner. Having entered this latest incident in the log the Skipper called off his vendetta with the deck and made straight for his cabin. The Bosun came up to take command of the bridge and brought a reliable helmsman (Wacker) with him. He brought the ship round with great care, ensuring that the stern post stayed clear of drift-ice likely to jam between the post and the rudder. This manoeuvre in a restricted area is never easy and requires seamanship of a high order, with the engines maintaining just enough headway to enable the 200 ft. 0 in. long ship to be controlled by the helm.

Once round *Arctic Fox* edged her way back to clear water at 3 knots. The 'landscape' – both fore and aft – was most impressive. Animal life wanders everywhere across the wild waste of the Arctic pack-ice, but trawlers (when handled correctly) rarely approach as close to it as this. A number of seals lounging on tiny ice-floes glided on into the night. Seals work mostly beneath the ice, maintaining breathing holes through leads and crevices while keeping up a constant search for fish. These breathing holes are made wherever possible in the thin crust which can – and often does – become surrounded by ice up to ten feet thick. When this happens the seal stands to lose his life by freezing fast against the ice in the narrow tunnel. He must force himself up through this tunnel to take the air at the top, or hold his breath in the hope of finding a crevice elsewhere. If there is no crevice, or the hole freezes over, the seal will drown. Seals have been found within one degree of the Pole and more than 200 miles from land. Both regions are beyond the reach of trappers and it is believed the seals are aware of this fact. They must also be aware of the Polar bears, padding across the ice looking for them. The presence of bears on the Polar pack, hundreds of miles from shore, is a sign that the seals upon which they prey are present in the region. Behind the Polar bears come the Arctic foxes, jumping from one ice island to another, ready to eat up anything the bears leave behind. If the bears leave nothing for the foxes, they chase after the seals. In their search for food, foxes both blue and white, will also travel a hundred miles from the edge of the pack-ice, sometimes hunting in packs, at other times quite alone – their dry staccato bark being the only indication of their presence, so perfect is their camouflage. The silent Arctic gull is a constant companion. In company with gannets, willocks and puffins, the gulls fly level with the rail of the ship and if the ship stops – the gulls stop. They ride the wind and then tread backwards, pushing their short, orange legs against the drift before landing on the sea at exactly the right place by the scupper ports. Later, when full of fish entrails and liver, they run fast across the water and usually make two attempts before becoming airborne. The Arctic would be a lonely place without the gulls, who seem assured the trawlers are there for their benefit, although they never fly over a ship or come to rest on any part of it, except the rail. They sleep in groups on the water with their heads turned back into their feathers. They can walk across the water, but find it impossible to stand on or fly off the deck of a ship. Once blown inboard they are defenceless. At summer's end, the migratory instinct takes most of the animal population south of the Pole on the long journey across the barrens to winter in conditions favourable to their survival, although many die during the trek, particularly caribou. It is disappointing that the bears and foxes who remain and roam so far from land in search of prey can only be observed by searchlight – in total darkness.

It took *Arctic Fox* an hour to steam clear of the floe ice in contrast with the four and a half minutes taken earlier to cover the same distance. Once free she altered course north eastwards, with the coast of northern Norway 260 miles ahead and the southernmost point of Greenland 700 miles astern. Every available searchlight was trained for'ard and down on to the sea. Heavy spray cascaded off the stem and turned to powder on the wind. The heaving sea, pale green at one moment, translucent where the light broke the surface, pounded the ship without mercy. *Arctic Fox* had re-entered the storm. Boiling water flung over the side froze solid before it reached the sea. Ice built up on the ratlines, and the wind gusted at speeds up to 65 knots. The ocean felt vast, and boiled in a white fury. The bears watched the trawler leave the ice, standing in tired, elegant poses along the edge, their heads raised to catch the smell of fish from the empty pounds.

Arctic Fox was hoping for a drag out on fishing grounds which had proved profitable in the past but were known to take heavy toll of gear. One lost trawl worth £600 plus the cost of one day at sea – a further £400 – would turn two days' non-stop fishing into a total loss.

On reaching the Barents Sea, *Arctic Fox* was surprised to find that she was not alone. As a matter of fact, she narrowly missed ramming the other ship owing to a snow blizzard obliterating the Radar screen. The other ship was a modern diesel trawler, hove to without lights. *Arctic Fox* came to and put about, ready to come alongside as near as safety allowed. Here, once again, was the mystery trawler. With all available lights brought to bear, *Arctic Fox's* Skipper studied this strange vessel through glasses, whilst the Sparks clicked away with a Polaroid land camera. The photograph showed practically nothing, due to poor light, except the white letters painted on her stack. Through a magnifying glass the letters showed up sufficiently to make first-hand identification possible. The mystery ship *was* British, and her port of registry was Hull.

The news flashed across the Arctic, and soon brought a reply back to *Arctic Fox's* radio room which gave a somewhat sinister air to this ship's presence. She had been observed earlier, a mile off shore at North Cape, attended by a cutter seen to come out from a small fishing village hard by. This village had long been the subject of gossip and speculation by Norwegian pilots and skippers. Persistent rumours had all maintained that an anti-Norwegian spy group operated from the village, and had done so for many years. Part of their activities was believed to be concerned with the interception of coded signals which were later passed to the country whose interests they served. As the coast line fronting this village provided opportunity to observe the movements of the Nato fleet at exercise and gave equal access to the Soviet navy, certain inferences were bound to be made. Such inferences did not, however, help in explaining the presence of R.N. officers aboard the mystery ship, and as there was no evidence at all to suggest they were aboard on *this* occasion the possibility was finally discounted.

At this point the strange vessel disappears for ever. She turned away from *Arctic Fox* at her best speed, showing her stern for a minute or more when she revealed a further curious fact. Her name and port of registry had been painted out, but she was wearing the Ensign from a staff at the stern and it was tied in a knot. It is customary to wear the Ensign when entering or leaving port or to run it up ready for dipping when approaching any units of the Royal Navy. It is not the custom – among trawlers, at any rate – to wear the Ensign at any other time. 'Knotting the flag' is a practice adopted by east coast ships (Hull and Grimsby) when entering port, to indicate to the Customs launch that the trawler has some spirits and/or tobacco still under Bond and awaiting the seal. It has no known relevance apart from this. Whatever relevance it might or might not have had on this occasion will most probably never be known.

No one saw the mystery trawler again.

CHAPTER EIGHTEEN

On *Arctic Fox's* bridge the anti-spray cover of the voice pipe was eroded green by the sea. A few days earlier it had been bright enough to mirror the bristle on a man's chin. Now the sea had changed it.

The Skipper lifted the cover and withdrew the stopper. Slowly he stood erect before snapping the cover shut. He stepped forward until his face was pressed hard against the clear vision panel, then he shaded his eyes and watched the foredeck as it plunged in a sudden angular dive. They were very blue, very clear eyes. Eyes that measured things before they alerted the face. Eyes that looked at things for a long – and considering – moment before they reacted at all. He lifted his gaze and studied the bows as they slammed the ocean, sending spindrift forty feet into the air. The deck rolled through a 70 degree arc, and the Skipper's feet shifted to meet it. He waited for *Arctic Fox* to regain her trim, then he turned on the ship's Tannoy. After a pause he spoke into it.

'Is the Chief on the mess-deck?'

The reply came back: 'No. He's in the cabin, Skipper.'

'Tell him I want him on the bridge.'

The Skipper pushed up the sender key and waited. There was

the ring of boot studs on the bridge ladder, and the Chief Engineer stood in the doorway. He spoke first.

'Well?'

'Perfectly. That's not why I called you.'

The Chief pulled the sweat rag from round his neck and wiped his hands. The Skipper stood still, recognising a symptom. There wasn't going to be a dénouement.

'This ship,' the Skipper began quietly, 'is leaking.'

'We're doing all we can. It's difficult to get at.' The Chief's tone was defensive. 'There's no lights down there – that doesn't help.'

'How long is it since you made an inspection?'

'I've been down there this watch. One of the Deenies went down last time we hauled.'

'And?'

'As far as I can say the level's about the same. Probably down a bit. As I say, it's difficult to see.'

The Skipper gripped the bridge rail and let the silence build up. Without turning he asked casually:

'Know what our draught is?'

The Chief thought for a moment.

'I should say 16 ft. It's on the specification.'

'It's in the Registry as well. That wasn't what I asked you.'

'Well, say 16 ft. or thereabouts.'

The Chief rubbed his chin with his knuckles. The bridge tilted and shuddered as the ship failed to breast the sea.

'Think again.'

'Perhaps if you told me what you were getting at—?'

By way of reply the Skipper drew a piece of paper from his pocket and smoothed it flat on the log table. Picking up a pencil he made a number of calculations. He turned to face the Chief before he replied.

'We haven't drawn 16 ft. for the last thousand miles.'

'We haven't?'

'No. We've been drawing 29 feet!'

The Chief's amazement was genuine.

'We can't have been – it's not possible.'

94

The Skipper leaned forward with both elbows resting on the long table. All along he had reasoned, thought, reacted and spoken with a cool mind. The price this had exacted was never revealed. Perhaps there was no price. Perhaps what happened next was the sheer anger of a man who had been let down once too often.

'I'll tell you something.' The Skipper turned and lifted his face level with the Chief's. 'The leak is between the collision bulkhead and the stem.'

'I know that. In the chain locker.'

'*No. Not* in the chain locker. IN THE FOREPEAK!! It entered the chain locker because the ballast tank has given way. *I* know that just by standing here. *You* don't because you never troubled to find out. Now – through your neglect to do what you're paid to do – we've lost our reserve buoyancy for'ard. *Look* at her.' The Skipper pointed to the bows. 'She stays in any position the sea cares to throw her. And if you don't know what *that* means I'll tell you.' The Skipper took a step forward. 'It means that once a sea broaches her to we're gone.' He snapped his fingers.' Just like that. WE'RE GONE.'

'I took it for granted . . .'

'YOU CAN'T TAKE ANYTHING FOR GRANTED OUT HERE – AND YOU HAD NO FUCKING RIGHT TO. Your experience should have told you that if the locker's full of sea water it must – have – come – from – somewhere – else. Either upwards from the keel or for'ard from the stem. If it's the keel it floods aft and your bilge pumps would be working overtime. If it's from the stem it finds its own level – UPWARDS. I'll give you fair warning, Chief, if the sea reaches the fish room—' The Skipper dropped his voice to a lower register. 'I'll – break – you. If it's the last thing I ever do.'

'How could *I* know . . . ?'

'IT'S YOUR DUTY TO FIND OUT. YOU'RE *paid* TO KNOW! MEN'S LIVES DEPEND ON IT. Come here!'

The Chief crossed to the front of the bridge.

'Have you ever seen this ship with a head trim like that before?'

'Can't say that I have, no.'

'I *know* you haven't. She's down by the head by ten extra feet.

The sea's lapping the rails – ALL DUE TO YOUR FUCKING INCOMPETENCE.'

'I'm not taking that from you – or anyone!'

The last moment of anger was the greatest.

'GET OFF THE BRIDGE – AND *stay* OFF!'

Roused from their bunks, the two off-duty engineers made ready and joined the two on watch. Fully rigged they made their way across the foredeck and descended the forehold. Drifting upwards, a whole bouquet of odours. Pitch, new rope, anti-corrosion paint, lead primer – and the sea. From where they stood the hatch covers of the lower hold were under water. Already it reached their thighs. They plunged their hands under the icy water and pulled the two halves of the cover clear. The sea was gushing in from the pointed triangular section forming the bows. Inspection lamps were lowered and secured by crocodile clips to the angle braces joining the cross members to the hull casing. Twenty feet of pump suction line were lowered and set to work. A portable motor pump was rigged, and its pull cord wound round the flywheel. More hose was brought, and the donkey started up. A two-way hand pump was lowered, and soon every bit of suction equipment *Arctic Fox* possessed was working at full pressure.

CHAPTER NINETEEN

The region above the Circle is a powerful and secure world, exclusive and self-sustaining within its own forbidding boundaries. A world of undeniable beauty and sensations of sublimity. Its inhuman wastes often reveal a savage splendour and strange, fragmentary glimpses of the beginning – and possibly the ending ? of the long reach of time. When the clouds part in winter the starlit ocean gives a meaning to infinity.

Despite exploration and Polar flight, much of the Polar world remains an untrodden land. Most of the region to the north of the American Continent is unknown and unnavigable. The interior of the North Polar Basin is still uncharted and unexplored. The environment of the Arctic remains the least altered by man.

In winter, landfast ice extends seaward, reaching Lat. 74 degrees North. Long. 144 degrees West – well out into the Arctic Ocean, growing steadily as the grip of winter rolls across the Tundra Plain, freezing the sea into an ice desert. Wild animals roam this wilderness, sometimes all their lives. Seals remain the most tame of wild life, and foxes the great predators. Bears bring humour to a lifeless Continent, and the sea unicorn is a living fable. With a fair wind blowing out of the north, wolves follow reindeer in silent arcs and circles towards the Pole. The seas are the coldest and clearest seas in the world.

Summers are short, with twenty-three hours of daylight. There is sunshine at midnight, and in July the twilight waits to meet the dawn. Forty-six days separate spring and the new winter, and the highest elevation the sun is ever likely to reach at summer solstice is $23\frac{1}{2}$ degrees. On the warmest day of the warmest month (July) the temperature climbs above 0 degrees Centigrade across the North Polar Sea, and from a trawler one can hear the distant roar of surf eroding the Great Ice Barrier.

Early in July the orange chrome ball of the sun moves nearer the horizon and the nights grow longer – and by September winter has returned. The first snows fall like a gentle Benediction, and soon all the world is white. In December the sun touches the rim of the sea for the last time and then drops with casual grace below the horizon. All is oblivion. The desperate winter begins. Now, man and beast will live in perpetual darkness for 115 days – alone against the great cold, breathing air colder than the Polar Ice Cap itself, colder than the ice-packed Arctic Sea – colder, almost, than man can endure. Stunted trees bow to the power of savage winds. Ice-floes one hundred feet thick circle the Pole in slow motion. On the edge of the Polar Sea the frozen remains of female caribou lie as though asleep in the loneliness of Arctic night. Preserved – preserved for ever, maybe. Preserved until the Ice Age comes again and gives them life.

Everywhere is empty. Infinite and timeless. For time, man's measure of his own existence, means nothing here. Silence descends upon the barren grounds – and silence itself has a metallic ring, broken only by the bark of white foxes (not yet to grace the shoulders of rich women) as they dig in ice as hard as iron to reach the carcass of musk oxen and eat their entrails. Arctic gulls flutter like white flower petals and then stand to attention along the ship's rail, waiting – waiting for fish which they gut with a surgeon's skill. Above, in the domed arc of the black sky, the Aurora Borealis shimmers like gossamer against a background of stars flung across the Heavens like a veil of diamonds. Below, glittering icebergs voyage across the black water.

Nothing changes in the Arctic. Only the seasons. And as the grip of winter tightens on land and sea, and both night and day follow each other in silent darkness, only the bulkhead clock on the mess-deck tells the crew it's morning again. And then it's night. Another day passes . . .

The word 'Arctic' is derived from the Greek 'Arktos': the bright star in the Great Bear constellation which encircles the sky in north Polar regions. Seen from the southernmost tip of Greenland this lone star glitters like sapphire and crystal in a halo of silver dust, and is sometimes seen through a single wide scimitar of light pulsating against the sky before dissolving in a curtain of green fire.

To the Eskimoes, this is the turning point of winter. Soon, the waste of ice in the changeless desert would start in motion, the voice of the storm fall to a whisper and the ebb tide draw the glaciers out to sea. The pack ice, swelled by every wind from every valley and every forgotten sea, would hurry to catch the glacial current from the Pole. The seal would appear from the deep ocean, the bears shake themselves in snowy hollows, and the fox would be alone no longer. The ptarmigan would have won the fight to stay alive in a waste of snow and ice, and start to lay eggs in the glacier-carved valleys.

But meanwhile, winter is supreme – and nothing moves except to die. Only the hardy gull, storm driven, caught by the wind, thrown until its wings break and trail beside it like oars, refuses to efface itself before unrelenting nature. Only the gull – and man.

Arctic Fox and her crew were barely to touch the rim of this strange world, but the glimpses it gave would always remain.

CHAPTER TWENTY

Having laid off new bearings, the Skipper emerged from the chartroom and called the Bosun to the bridge. After receiving fresh orders Barry left, reluctant to discuss what he had been told. The Skipper crossed the bridge to the port wing, pausing to glance at the reflector compass binnacle set in the deckhead. With his face pressed hard against the clear vision panel, the Skipper carefully searched the sky. It was black and empty. Bullets of ice fell like a bead curtain down on to the deck. The Radar showed no land, only a cluster of ships steaming fast to the south. Within an hour they would be many miles astern, and *Arctic Fox* would be alone on an empty sea. Black Frost was closing in, and everywhere the relentless wind, the cold and ever-changing, treacherous ocean.

Within an hour all three had increased in force, in anger and in intensity. The ship eased in to 3 knots, and the wheel was put hard over.

Under the fo'c's'le head a couple of massive iron bobbins were adrift, rolling from side to side, smashing against the bow plates. As the ship careened the rolling became a frenzy and the clangs echoed and reverberated along the hull in hollow waves like the final chords of some forbidding symphony. As the ship regained her centre of buoyancy, only one bobbin remained free. In the engine room – twelve feet below the water line – it boomed in the lower registers of sound, making the two men cover their ears in an attempt to keep it out. To one of them it sounded like a ship's bell. The other thought it was a mine.

The Mate, resting on the red leather seat locker in his one-man berth, sensed the alteration in the ship's course and perhaps he wondered why he'd not been told about it. As the floor tilted to starboard, he rolled to his feet and sat back in a chair before lighting a cigarette. The galley boy knocked and entered with a pot of tea.

'Stick it down there, kiddo . . . wedge it against something.'

'Want some biscuits, Ken?'

'No. You're all right, Sunshine, that'll do.'

'The weather's rough – it's blowing like a bastard, Ken.'

'It never does anything else out this way in winter.'

'Yes – I've noticed that.'

'Bang the door behind you, kiddo, otherwise it won't stay shut.'

'O.K. then.'

Despite his Skipper's ticket the Mate had never lost his identity as a rough and ready deckman, and the crew respected him for it. They respected, too, his natural air of authority. It was a tough, uncompromising authority, but the crew accepted it. Their hardships were his hardships, and through sharing them they respected him more than they loathed him. He couldn't hope for more because he was that kind of man, and the crew was that kind of crew. He played a dangerous game to the limit. Exposed his men and himself to extremes of hardship with no quarter and no thanks. Sometimes he should have ordered them from the deck sooner than he did. Sometimes he was wrong to destroy a man's self-confidence with his brutal invective. His anger was often unjust. He was coarse and lacked subtlety, but men understood him. They knew he was working for their good as well as his own, and he was incapable of malice. Without him there was no partnership of feeling – actions were less galvanic because they lacked the confidence he gave to them. Above all, he fitted their picture of what a Mate ought to be like – the way they imagined themselves one day – swearing at the sea and the wind. Holding on and fighting back when lesser men

100

would have abandoned the deck. Roaring and laughing with death pulling him nearer to her side, and then – sensing what the occasion demanded – bursting into song and ordering everyone to join in the chorus. The crew might not like him, but they accepted what he stood for and that was a very great deal. Without him *Arctic Fox* would have been a different ship, because the crew thought of him as a part of her fighting existence. Justly or unjustly, they never thought of the Skipper in that way. In their eyes he was not a mariner in the way the Mate was a mariner. He was up there – on the bridge making decisions no one got to hear about until told to carry them out.

The Skipper and the Mate met at dinner. These two contemporaries in a highly competitive world sat facing each other across the table in the officers' dining cabin. The food was the same as that served on the mess-deck, but the atmosphere most decidedly was not. The Mate had fought and lost many a private battle across this table, and now it seemed he was about to fire the opening shots in yet another.

'You *must* know.'

'Know what?' The Skipper hadn't heard the question.

'Are we steaming far or not?'

'It depends.'

'On what?'

'On what happens.'

'What are we playing – some kind of guessing game?'

'That's all I know.'

'About what?'

'My intentions are to bring us on to some fish.'

'That's presumably been your intention all along, so where are we going *now*?'

The Skipper took a buster from the table and began, resentfully, to spread the butter.

'Farther north.'

'For a sun tan? A swim? Slave trading amongst the Eskimoes?'

'No. Fishing,' replied the Skipper after a pause.

'Well, that'll make a change.'

If the Skipper was aware of a budding antagonism he didn't show it. He began . . .

'I don't think you have the right . . .' and then thought better of it. 'Is that soup in that jug?'

'You couldn't have got reports from wherever it is you're going!'

'No – we've not got any reports.'

'Because no one's been up that far?'

'Not as far as that, no.' The Skipper obviously didn't like the Mate's growing ascendancy, but equally he didn't know how to counter it without giving his reasons for having made the decision in the first place.

'This new ground – is it properly charted?'

'There's nothing here. It's worth a try.' Having delivered himself of this impressive enigma, the Skipper pushed his soup plate towards the waiting galley boy and sat back.

'You know nothing about it, then?'

'It's the same kind of ground as Fuglöy and Malangen Bank. Rather clean, a few rocks, I expect, and patches of mud.'

'We lost a complete trawl on the north-west bank, including the doors. That's the same ground as Fuglöy, and no better than Skraaven.'

'There'll be fish where we're going, if we're lucky.'

Suddenly alert, suddenly ironic, the Mate flashed back – 'We'll need to be that.'

Coolly, after a pause, the Skipper answered, 'Yes. Any Jockey's Whips in that dish?'

The Mate leaned forward and evenly, without expression, asked 'Have you actually *laid* a course or are we water divining again?'

'The course lines,' answered the Skipper, adroit as quicksilver, 'are a guide – we may turn away from them in a few hours, or later. It depends on what happens when we find bottom.'

'Is this Paradise you're taking us to navigable?'

Still refusing the barb, the Skipper answered, 'I've considered the ice. We can get through.'

'*And* back?'

'I would think so. Depends rather on the strength of the

currents and whether the pack's broken into drifts. If that happens with the wind above Beaufort Nine we'll have to play it smart.'

The Mate said nothing.

The Skipper added, 'It's worth a gamble'.

'Is that how you see it?' said the Mate immediately.

'That's how everyone regards trawling, isn't it?'

The meal continued in silence. The Mate admitted the justice of this remark by his refusal to reply, and his menacing attitude softened a little. In these out-of-the-way latitudes one man's judgement was as good as another's. The ground hadn't been worked before, not even by the Russians. It might pay off. It might . . .

'When do we get there?'

'I should set steaming watches for the time being, Ken, and bring the doors in. The trawl needn't be lashed up. Just make sure it's secure. That's all.'

The Mate tried again.

'You should have told me. I've a right to know.'

'Well, you know now.'

With that the Skipper stood up. Both men faced each other. Then, as if by mutual accord, each turned away. As usual, the Mate had got nowhere. Barry would tell him the rest when he came off watch – and 'the rest' would follow the same carefully ambiguous pattern. Barry didn't ask questions the way the Mate did, but waited to be told. Somehow he always knew more. The Skipper might almost have guessed his Mate's thoughts, judging by his final remark.

'Ken, tell Barry I want him.'

The Mate replied from half way up the companion ladder. A smell of damp rubber rose in his wake.

The mess-deck was full, and those of the crew on 'second sitting' were hanging about in the gangway. The Mate brushed past them, ignoring their questions, until he stood on the mess-deck.

'What we doing, Ken? Anything or owt?' someone asked.

'Steaming,' the Mate replied curtly. 'I want all hands for two o'clock. We're taking the doors in and changing bridles.'

'Does that include the Watch Below?' questioned Paddy.

'ALL HANDS means *everbody* – including you, you Irish peasant.' (The word 'peasant' was spoken with relish.)

'Where we going?' enquired Colin.

'North. To do some sun-bathing.'

'*Not* the White Sea?'

The Mate didn't reply.

The Badger, with his gobbling irons knotted to a piece of twine round his neck and a red spotted handkerchief tied to serve as a bib, stopped eating long enough to take in what was going on. Looking straight at the Mate he remarked: 'I reckon you knew nothing half an hour ago and you know fuck all now.'

'Enough of your lip, Badger. Stow it.'

Ignoring the rebuke, the Badger went on: 'We're going to South Spitsbergen to look for cod.'

'If you know that,' the Mate's voice sounded truculent, 'you know more than I do.'

'That' – there was a pause while the Badger forked all the meat off the Whippit's plate on to his own – 'wouldn't surprise me a bit.'

'You're a right gobbie bastard, Badger.'

The Badger harpooned three large potatoes before replying.

'I am and all,' he said with a soft chuckle, 'but we're still going to Spitsbergen, and if I'm wrong I'll give you my new sou'wester.'

'You haven't *got* a new sou'wester.' A number of voices spoke in unison.

'No,' replied the Badger in his most reasonable and helpful voice, 'but the Whippit has.'

The Mate wouldn't have been human if he'd not wanted to hear how the Badger knew they were going to Spitsbergen, but if he asked now he would reveal his failure to find out for himself. The next question sharpened his face into sudden awareness. Harry spoke: '*You've* been told – what's wrong with telling us?'

'The Skipper's not sure yet.' The Mate's tone was convincing, partly because he'd repeated the truth, but perhaps he was hoping to draw the Badger back into the conversation.

Harry altered his approach.

'But you're setting steaming watches, aren't you?'

'I am.'

'How long for?'

'You're a dayman, so I shouldn't bother . . .'

Harry cut across the reply with a precise question.

'Is it Spitsbergen, then, Ken?'

The Mate answered with a calmness his features failed to reflect: 'I shouldn't think that's likely.'

'You don't know, then?'

'NO ONE knows!'

At this point the Badger could have moved in and finished the whole thing off. Quickly, brutally and for good. But he waited, seemingly disinterested, obviously thinking things out. Wondering, perhaps, if it was worth the trouble it would cause. Paddy took up the questioning: 'What's so bastard secret about it, anyway?' His voice was cheerfully sarcastic. 'Is anyone else up there?'

'No one.'

'It *is* Spitsbergen, then?'

There was a shallow silence broken only by the Badger shovelling up tapioca swimming in treacle. A dozen faces looked up at the Mate, waiting for an answer. Presently they calmed down, sitting in silent, sullen thought. One by one they began to grumble, quietly, reasonably, as if the Mate was no longer there.

'There's no bastard charts for one thing.'

'It's charted – all that area's charted – but it's covered with pack ice.'

'There'll be leads, though. We could get through.'

'What if there's no fish?'

'The old man's got his reasons.'

'You'd think he'd tell *someone*.'

'Since when have you sailed with a Skipper who tells you what he's doing next?'

'I'm saying he should let us *know*.'

'Go and fucking ask him then.'

'. . . the Mate knows.'

'*Do* you know, Ken?'

105

The Mate spoke thoughtfully. 'Our intentions are . . .'

The Badger produced an apple from inside his shirt and polished it with his muffler: '*Your* intentions' he interrupted, 'are to keep everyone guessing – like laughing boy up there. You're the best tightrope walker in the business.'

The Mate spun round. His face showed he was in no mood to stand that kind of insult.

'Open your gob once more . . .'

'THEN TELL US WHAT YOU'VE AGREED TO. WE WANT TO *know*.'

The Badger's roar would provoke any man – after all, it was meant to do just that. The Mate knew this. He said nothing. He wavered just for a moment before passing his hand over his face. Leaning forward, he looked as though he might – he just might – crumple his fist and draw his muscular arm away from his body. Instead, he sat down. In abrupt, short sentences, he told them all he knew – he neither defended nor criticized, he merely explained. When he'd finished everyone knew what they were in for. They understood – but they didn't like it.

The snarls set in. Fo'c's'le backchat descended to bickering. The forced air ventilation blew hot and cold as angry fingers turned it this way and that. Paddy flung a plate through the hatch, hitting All Sorts in the back. A knife flashed, and the Badger moved in and took it away. The Sparks who, when away from the bridge, assumed the function of command, remarked, 'I say, lads, that bridge top simply *ha*s to be de-iced if I'm to keep anything running'. The boot thrust in the small of his back flung him against Bill. A punch in the kidneys made him forget the bridge top. Someone had taken Barry's paperback. He was calm, but he wanted it back. Harry called Buster 'a card sharp'. The remark was familiar enough, but for once no one laughed. Yorkie threw some waste rag which fell on the Whippit. The Whippit didn't fight on board ship, but at sea there's a first time for everything. By tea time, the self-contained life on the small ship had grown distinctly ugly. Later it became worse. As if to remind them of something they wanted to forget until it hit them, the wind blew screaming off the Polar Ice Cap and tore at everything it could reach. The ship shuddered, and down below the engineers flinched as she rolled over. Rightly – because they worked below the waterline – they experienced a twinge of alarm. With their watch over, these two men climbed the catwalk and entered the mess-deck. Immediately, the deckmen fell on them like wolves. The engineers had been scared, and they still showed it.

'Yellow bastards.'

'Bilge rats.'

'Couple of windy haggis-bashers.'

There was a fight. The Badger lifted one contestant off the floor and crashed him against the bulkhead. Turning to deal with the others, he found they'd gone. Soon there was shouting and pushing in the gangway outside until, one by one, they broke up and made for the crew's fo'c's'le. Here they brooded, with nothing to do. For some there was a desire to crush something – smash a beer can flat with one fist. Others remembered their grievances and wondered about their women. The oversexed read books – pornographic ones of course – to feed the hunger whose demands could not be satisfied.

Outside the storm raged with renewed fury, and the temperature fell to a deadly 73 degrees below freezing point. Beneath the fo'c's'le the sea lapped the combing of the lower hold and raced like a slowly opening fan towards the net bins. As men slept, it rose beneath them. By dawn it had fallen again.

It was 5 a.m. In the chart room the Skipper corrected the bearing and laid it off on the chart. Moments later *Arctic Fox* turned under a full helm and listed sharply as the revolutions mounted. At a few minutes past six in the morning a tiny object appeared at the upper edge of the Radar screen. No bigger than a pin dot, flickering blue and then fading. The Skipper, hunched in a dark corner of the bridge, crossed to the set. For a number of minutes he studied the single small echo before leaning back to read the compass.

'Steer two points to starboard.'

The Badger, recalling for the hundredth time that the Skipper never addressed him by name, put the wheel over and let the spokes run back through his fingers.

'Don't you acknowledge?'

'What, for instance?'

'We've just altered course, haven't we?'

The Badger repeated, adopting his most chilling manner 'Alter 22 degrees 30 minutes starboard. On course' – he squinted at the clock – 'at five to three – precisely, Captain, Sir.'

The Skipper quickly buried his head back in the Radar.

'Come here and look at this.' His tone was abrupt – he would have preferred not to consult the Badger, but he wanted the echo confirmed. The Badger lumbered across and peered down inside the viewing hood.

'Well?'

The Badger's reply was muffled: 'I reckon we've got a gannet sitting on the aerial again.'

Had the bridge been soundproof he would have heard its other occupant grinding his teeth.

By mid-day the luminous detached echo had grown to a solid pattern, spreading like a cancer in *Arctic Fox's* path. Long before the smell of fresh bread brought a reminder of tea, the solid pattern became a mass. Then it was a continent – white, flat and endless. At 3 a.m. the snow was a raging blizzard, and the continent didn't show up. *Arctic Fox* sheered wildly all that night. Twenty times she fell off, and twenty times she was hauled back again. As breakfast time came round again the wind fell and the snow managed only an occasional flurry. The Radar was usable once more. One glance was enough. Dead ahead and along both sides, moving steadily south, the great ice barrier of the Arctic Seas. On the foredeck men's boots left footprints in the snow before the sea rushed in and gave absolution.

On the bridge, the Badger held an empty glass. At nine o'clock the Skipper issued the rum. Down in the engine room the Chief wiped his face and neck before hurrying to answer the voice pipe. Moments later he turned and waved his fireman towards the soundproof hood.

'We're twenty miles off the barrier – should be there in an hour and forty minutes.'

On the mess-deck the Whippit finished what must have been his third breakfast. Two tins of corned beef, half a pound of cheese and a whole jar of onions. To wash it down he produced a can of beer from inside his shirt, and then he pulled out two more. Sitting back, he remarked to no one in particular: 'Better fuck off before the engineers come off watch – they'll think I've eaten all the grub.'

'It's rumoured' – Harry looked over the top of his comic at the Whippit – 'that you only come out this way for the grub.'

The Whippit emptied his last can of beer and yawned. From the gangway outside, he half turned and shouted back: 'So long as you're not paying for it . . .'

Hunched forward on the bridge, legs braced against the telegraph pedestal, the Skipper raised his glasses and focussed them on a distant unseen line where the ocean met the sky. Presently he frowned and leaned forward into the Radar. Slowly, relentlessly, like a ghost in the night, the vast irregular mass of the ice barrier crept over the screen.

'Should be getting a sighting anytime now.'

Barry half turned from the port lookout to reply.

'Aye, I reckon, Skipper.'

Turning to the Badger the Skipper suddenly asked: 'What's your course?'

The Badger confirmed: 'Nor' Nor' East.'

'Nothing off. Watch her head.'

The Badger repeated: 'Nothing off. Keep her right on.'

On the bridgetop the scanner swept an unseen horizon. There was nothing to do but wait. Somehow that was the hardest part of all.

It appeared, ages later, two points off the starboard bow, looking like a thin, white line. Ten minutes afterwards its firm, unbroken cliffs thrust sharply from the darkness all around it. Ice smoke descended like a blanket over the ship and then fell away on the wind. Suddenly, the barrier was visible – solid, edging nearer. It was strange how a world empty of colour could hold such barbarous splendour. The Skipper drew back from the bridge window, his face without expression.

'This is it.'

The Mate clumped up the bridge ladder in time to hear the

remark, but said nothing. The waiting was over, and the bridge became the centre of activity.

The Skipper had the knack – unnoticed before – of moving quickly without seeming to hurry. All at once there was something special in the way he handled the complex equipment and gave his quiet orders.

'Steer five degrees starboard.'

Turning aside he pressed a button, and bells rang throughout the ship. A surge of feeling rose up everywhere. The austere command which followed exactly suited the occasion.

'All hands on deck.'

For a flickering instant one sensed, almost with a feeling of shock, that this strange man really could command, and could do so with a quiet ruthlessness which made men fear him without knowing why.

'Ken.'

The Mate's shoulders stiffened instinctively.

'Yes?'

'Cut the trawl free of its lashings and get ready to shoot away.'

'Are we keeping the thirty foot bridles?'

The Skipper, answering him, said softly: 'You know we are.'

Flushing with anger the Mate shouted back: 'I only bloody well asked.'

With that lack of emphasis which was such an effective substitute the Skipper replied: 'Now you've been told.'

Things happened quickly after that, but it was not until the crew broke on to the deck from the fo'c'sle and began to take up stations – some drawing off aft – that they saw the great ice barrier. They'd all been expecting *something* – but not something like this. On three sides was a vast plain, terrifying in its level whiteness. It was cold – colder than it had ever been. The wind tore at their faces, and the snow blinded them. The air was filled with tiny stilettos of ice which froze on the mouth, around the eyes and the chin. Axes were needed to free the Cod End frozen to the deck. Fish dropped out from its folds and fell to the deck with the thud of iron.

The weather was rough all right. But it wasn't the weather

the crew was concerned with. It wasn't the wilderness of the great ice barrier – although that was impressive enough. It was the ocean which made every man's thoughts run to a pattern. Throughout the ship men watched it as it tried to engulf them. It seemed to be saying: 'You've no right to be here, but now that you are . . . !' Great cliffs of green water forty feet high came scything through the night and buried everything they could reach. On the deck, men blundered about holding on to each other before being torn apart and slammed violently back. The ship – a thousand tons of iron, wood, metal and men – shuddered with the force of it all.

Quickly, seeing the danger, the Skipper grasped the telegraph handle and thrust it down. Deep inside the ship a bell rang and *Arctic Fox* eased in until she almost lost steerage way. Abruptly, the Skipper rapped out a command.

'Starboard ten. Steer north.'

As the ship sheered away from the great ice barrier the black frost parted and her foremost searchlight showed the contorted ridges glistening with spurs. Twenty-ton blocks rafted and reared on top of each other before rending apart. Everywhere there was a sustained roar as this lethal continent of tormented ice heaved under the hidden pressures of the ocean. The roar penetrated the engine room and rose above the noise of the 1,200 horse-power engine. It smashed a half-inch plate-glass mirror into fragments, and fractured all the boiler gauge glasses.

As *Arctic Fox* circled and began to smash ahead, one again became aware of the air of decision and command now flowing from the bridge. On the port wing the Sparks eased his back and stood erect with his eyes staring forward and down. The bridge rolled through a 70 degree arc and the Sparks rolled with it. Fear had first touched his shoulder an hour or two previously when he realised *Arctic Fox* had lost radio contact with the outside world. From this private tide mark his courage began to ebb. Privately – he was to make it public later on – this was the moment when he decided he would never again set foot on board a trawler.

From his customary position by the starboard window, the

Skipper relaxed his grip on the brass rail and turned to read the compass in the deckhead. Satisfied, he dismissed the Badger from the helm with a curt nod, and got an equally curt one in reply. With a loud 'Whoof' of joy the Badger clambered down the bridge ladder and hurried to get rigged. A little while later his massive, reassuring bulk was lumbering about the deck giving encouragement (but very little actual assistance) to the deckmen struggling to prepare the trawl ready for the waiting ocean.

Arctic Fox canted to port, and then back to starboard again. The path she had opened up lay visible behind her as she turned her tough, elegant bows to the ice-filled sea. The single star overhead watched without pity and then – when the sextant was brought and made ready – it faded into the snow-filled darkness. The alcohol thermometer registered 68 degrees below zero – 100 degrees of frost. Not far short of the *Ant*arctic record, and cold enough for instant death.

This was trawling at its worst. In this kind of weather a man had only to lose his grip and he'd be gone – within 60 seconds he would be dead, frozen into a grotesque shape before the sea could drown him. Before he hit the water the cold would bring exquisite pain, numbing the flesh. Moments later the blood in the body would start to freeze – and then oblivion.

CHAPTER TWENTY-ONE

On the bridge the Skipper took over the wheel. His shoulders moved rhythmically as the ship fell off and was hauled back on again. His face, disembodied in the light from the compass binnacle, was set forward from his body, staring dead ahead. He spoke without taking his eyes from the bows: 'We'll go about soon as we're a cable or two from the moving ice . . . that'll take the way off her, and we'll stand off before running back over the ground. That sounder's gone on the blink again and there's no fathom depth on the charts we've got.'

Arctic Fox heeled to the wind as the spokes of the wheel ran back through the Skipper's fingers.

'Let's hope we don't hit anything.'

In the engine room there was a feeling of remoteness from danger, but water was running in from the started rivet-holes and the sea was just beginning to sluice up out of the bilges. Both engineers were bending over the pump when *Arctic Fox* struck and came to a long, grinding halt. She tore herself loose almost at once. Everywhere was alive with the pounding of the engines, as though her pulse beat knew this wasn't the end. The berg fell back in the wind torn darkness. The stern plunged deep beneath the ocean.

'Stop engines!'

The Sparks leapt to the telegraph.

'Bloody hell, we've struck a submerged berg – we've hit a bloody iceberg!'

He suddenly turned and stared at the echo sounder.

'Skip, look!'

'What?'

'The sounder – we're nearly resting on an ice shelf!'

The fathom depth wasn't being sounded – it was being re-corded *by the keel scraping the ice.* The Sparks turned sharply away, trying unsuccessfully not to catch anyone's eye. The ocean clawed *Arctic Fox's* stern, and with the way off her she swung out away from the barrier.

'Ring her on! RING HER ON – SLOW AHEAD!'

Slowly, she moved into deep water. She won her sea room. She stood bows on to the great waves. This was her last iceberg.

One final disaster awaited her.

CHAPTER TWENTY-TWO

This would have been the moment for the Skipper to inspect his ship. He knew her in every detail from end to end. Knew with a sure, blind touch where to go and listen for trouble – where to stand to catch the odd vibration from an unaligned shaft; judge her trim through the soles of his shoes and go straight to a damaged hull plate or a started rivet in some black, unseen corner no one else had thought of. He could do this better than anyone aboard. He should have been doing it now.

The Skipper kept station on the bridge, leaning forward, elbows resting on the bridge rail, hands covering his ears. To all appearances he was doing what he had done so often before. He was watching the breaking sea – following its every move with his eyes wide open. The sea was fennel-green, racing before a driving wind; the kind of sea one remembers when there's occasion to recall the Arctic.

Lifting the cover of the voice pipe, the Skipper called the engine room.

'Chief? I want you on the bridge.'

When the Chief entered and spoke, the Skipper neither turned nor changed his position. His only movement was to remove one hand from his ear.

'I was saying,' the Chief repeated, 'that last bang shook us up down there. Jock and myself were trying to boost the suction rate on one of the bilge pumps and by the time we'd picked ourselves up you'd already rung down.'

The Chief tugged at the sweat rag round his neck.

'I stopped her fast as I could – wish it had been sooner . . .'

The Skipper turned and looked past him without comment Finally he spoke.

'I can't remember the time when you've come up here without offering excuses for something you've failed to do. What I'm waiting for is a report of the damage. Until I get it we'll haul round and back again. The longer you stand there the more fishing time we're losing so if all you want to do is chat I suggest you get below and find out if we're seaworthy.'

The Chief turned to leave.

'– and I can do without the "ifs and buts". What's needed are some cold, hard facts.'

'One day,' the Chief answered from the foot of the bridge ladder, 'one day, Captain, I'm going to be tempted into giving you some.'

Arctic Fox steered in great arcs and circles. The revolutions mounted as the searchlights lit the way ahead. The Great Bear showed itself for an instant, low in the Polar sky.

The Chief announced the ship was reasonably seaworthy and ready to proceed. Proceed she did, due west, in nil visibility.

Having ordered the crew to stand down and resume steaming watches the Skipper left the bridge to commence a long study of the charts.

The charts showed the limits and speed of flow of the pack ice which, if it closed round the ship, would crush her. This possibility had been accepted – not with the usual fatalism, but with the knowledge that the pack ice was known to move at about one-fifteenth the speed of the wind and veer 30 degrees to the right of the wind current.

Although the ground was poorly charted, with fathom markings inaccurate or non-existent, the area was likely to be rich in marine life. Cod fish favour the cooler waters like those of the mid-oceanic shelf which *Arctic Fox* was to pass over. Haddock prefer the warmer water farther north, but when fully grown turn southwards in winter to live in the same rocky ground frequented by the cod fish. In this region haddock were expected to feed in 'daylight', by running deep into 300 fathoms to search the ocean bed. The cod fish were likely to be found shoaling along above the haddock.

In these untried waters there were no signs for the experienced eye to read – the gathering birds, the porpoises arching their backs clear of the sea – indicating that fish were about. And the use of the phrase 'daylight fishing' would seem to pay more respect to man's chronometry than to the habits of fish in a region of endless night. It is not, in fact, the 'light' but the perceptible variation in the intensity of the darkness to which the fish responds, by altering its reaction to gravity; further encouraged by the natural tendency of anything heavier than water to sink down into it. As the 'light' goes (dawn breaks), the response to gravity changes and the haddock comes again to within 300 ft. of the water's surface. All these facts were known – not necessarily by the crew, but by the Skipper who had finally set aside his aversion to wholly 'scientific fishing' and discounted for once the 'folk lore bible' left behind by his grandfather.

As this area was rarely visited by trawlers and marked the most Pole-ward extension of fishing in the world, the fish – if they were found – would be abundant, and some of the largest of their kind ever to be caught. Cod fish – olive green or brown with dark spots and a sensitive barbel on the chin – take three years to grow to a length of 10 in. and another four years before they are 24 in. long. After twelve years in the sea they measure not more than 3 ft. 6 in. In an area such as this, they may live for twenty years and grow to a length of 5 ft. 0 in. Weights vary from 14 oz. to 40 lb. Fish of this weight and size make up the bulk of fish caught by distant water ships trawling on the better known, more heavily fished grounds. Haddock have a more rounded shape and are small, identified by the black St Peter's thumb mark on each side above the pectoral fin – where St Peter is supposed to have pulled the fish out of the Lake Gennesaret – a story retold by experienced, non-religious trawlermen regardless of the fact that the haddock did not and could not have lived in the lake. It is interesting that fishermen repeat this story to each other at sea and decline to do so among strangers ashore – not because its retelling exposes their fallibility to 'outsiders' and can be seen to contradict their experience as fishermen, but because it enriches one of the many superstitions which they acknowledge amongst themselves and are not willing to share with anyone else. Coal fish could be expected in this area during the winter season and would always be saleable ashore. The public meets the coalie more often than it imagines. Much of the cheaper fish sold in restaurants – often quite expensive ones – and fried fish shops is sold as cod, or simply as fish. Most of it is, in fact, coalie.

As a device for catching fish the trawl is a clumsy but effective method. Simple in theory, complex in design, difficult to handle at all times and needing the most careful launching in rough seas, it dominates the crew's existence and every movement of the ship. Easily damaged, difficult to mend, expensive to manufacture, it takes hours to replace when lost or torn to pieces. It has been cursed over, prayed over and angrily jumped on by every man who has ever been deep water fishing. Only one thing has never happened to it – it has never been re-designed to make it more simple and effective. With the passing of the conventional side trawler and the arrival of the stern freezer it is likely to stay the way it is. Whatever men think of it, it remains above everything else the most vital and the most valuable piece of equipment aboard a trawler. Like many simple things its function is not easily described, due mainly to it being invisible when it is actually working. The mouth of the net is attached at each side to the weighted, rectangular door. The two doors are towed through the water by the trawler's warp wires and are set at an oblique angle so that they diverge from one another, pulling open the mouth of the net. The lower lip of the mouth is held down by the footrope through which the metal rollers or bobbins are reeved. These enable the lower half of the trawl to run over the ocean bed and surmount rocks or other obstacles likely to stop its progress. The upper half of the trawl is kept open by the air-filled floats attached at short intervals to the headline. The sides of the mouth of the net are separated from the doors by the long wire bridles. When cast into the sea and travelling along the bottom, the complete trawl gives the appearance of a 'U' directed away from the forward movement of the ship so as to sweep into the conical end of the net any fish in its path. The bridles had earlier been replaced by ones of greater length and then changed back – for no particular reason – in favour of the originals. Later, these were taken off and the trawl was left without bridles altogether. Finally, after much argument, new ones were shackled up which were clearly more suited to the greater depth of water the ship would now be trawling in.

Taken altogether, *Arctic Fox* had the best rigged trawl

she had so far used, largely due to the Skipper who insisted on having things done his way. The span of the headline would now operate to its full extent, providing an opening 130 ft. 0 in. wide. It remained to be seen whether the fish would be impressed by the improved trawl or whether they were present at all.

Harry, as usual, didn't think so. He was standing watch on the mess-deck in company with the Whippit and Buster, neither of whom welcomed Harry's conversation. He never doubted he was right about everything, and clarified and ordered his opinions to a large unseen audience with defective hearing. He was doing so at this moment.

'A right bastard hole in this place. We'll catch nothing here, so he (meaning the Skipper) needn't try. The swag don't come to these parts – they don't like the shelf for one thing. The old man wants to go for a few flats out eastwards or chase them Jumbos off the North Cape – topside of that gully afore it runs off into the deep. I'm right, aren't I, Whippit?'

'Go and tell the old man, then – I'm busy' – darning his sea-boot stockings.

'Buster knows I'm right, don't you, Buster?'

'You know fuck all about anything, so shut up!'

Buster's eyes never left his comic. He was the only one who could silence Harry, and although no one believed anything he said, he was preferred as a talker and, when Harry was present, positively encouraged. Prodded by the Whippit, Buster had just started to recall the time when he had trawled up half a U-boat crammed with the bodies of her crew when Harry stood up and announced it was 5.30 a.m. and time to call out the watch below.

'I'll call the Badger and you can call the other two.'

Harry, with a shrewdness most unbecoming in a trawlerman, had once offered the remark that the Badger's character was his destiny. It was impossible to say whether or not Harry had digested this observation or whether he understood the Badger well enough for it to have any meaning. The Badger, with his complete lack of introspection, thought little of his 'destiny' and as he cared nothing for his reputation it must be assumed that he was not concerned with his character either.

118

Harry entered the Badger's berth, turned on the light, and stumbling over a prodigious amount of gear, he found the Badger's bunk and reached for the light. The Badger was lying back with his enormous bulk covered by a tartan blanket and his left hand gripping his 'still' – which was empty. After much shaking, he managed to defy the laws of gravity and sat up.

'You're on watch,' said Harry.

'What?'

'It's watch time!'

Even when drunk, Bob the Badger realised the ship must be kept going, and to this end he was prepared to make sacrifices.

'I'll get up.'

Back on the mess-deck Harry lost no time in giving the news to the other two. Adding with cruel finality: 'He won't be any fucking use but he'll put the numbers right.'

It so happened, however, that the Badger was not to stand watch on this occasion, as the bells rang throughout the ship at a few minutes to six and all hands were ordered on deck. Almost at once *Arctic Fox* eased in before turning to get the wind on the beam, ready to shoot away for the sixty-fifth time this trip. On the bridge, the telegraph rang – than rang again as the brass indicator joined the handle at Half Ahead. The Skipper turned away from the telegraph pedestal and studied the Radar where the screen showed the area to port covered with a plateau of ice stretching to the far horizon, its plain elevated five feet above water level. In this rarely visited area where fathom markings were not charted, the reliability of the self-recording echo sounder was important. Now, when it was most needed, it was found to be inaccurate. Air bubbles under the keel and the race of the propellers made its vertical reading so interrupted as to be useless. The Skipper had no choice but to ignore it and give his orders to the wheel, the helmsman (Paddy) repeating each one as it was given.

'Down two points.'

'Down two points.' Paddy put the helm over, and away from the wind.

'Down two points.'

'Is that a repeat, Skip?'

'Yes, she's still carrying away from the wind.'

'Down two points it is . . . she's not coming round, Skip,' bit more on the rudder?'

'Down a point.'

'Down one point.' The helm went further to leeward.

'Down half a point.'

'Down a half . . . she's slow to answer, Skip . . . I think she's falling away!'

'Keep her on that.'

'Aye, Skipper. She's falling to the lee, Skip!'

'Hard up and back, steady. I'll ring her on Full Ahead. Wait on the order.'

'Aye Aye.'

Arctic Fox gathered way until she was cleaving the water at near her best speed.

'Right! Hard a' weather NOW!'

'Hard up Skipper.'

Arctic Fox shot quickly to leeward.

'Hard over – and quick about it!'

Paddy put the ship over on a lee helm, but her head refused to pay off.

'She keeps throwing her head off, Skipper, running away from the wind.'

'Keep her on that. Nothing off.'

'Nothing off . . . she doesn't answer, Skip.'

'Right the helm!'

Paddy put the wheel midships and the rudder fell back in line with the keel. The Skipper rang the telegraph, and *Arctic Fox* came slowly to a stop. She was refusing to obey her helm. Despite the efforts made to bring her head up to the wind and make her stand on her point, she fell off every time. The increased headway was not enough to persuade the ship to be carried by her wheel except on a weather helm, when she payed off very fast to the lee and if allowed to yaw would crash into the ice. The ship had at last bowed to the weather. She was being alternately supported, first by one wave in the middle, then by two waves, one at each end. The bow and stern were lifting in phase and the midships section was lifting clear of the water independently. In addition, the five tons of water she had shipped since colliding with the ice barrier were acting as free running ballast in the bow, forcing her away from the wind each time Paddy tried to bring her up. With no room to manoeuvre *Arctic Fox* would now have to be put astern before her head could be payed off and the ship turned round.

The Bosun was brought on to the bridge to take the wheel whilst the Skipper gave his attention to the Radar screen. In going astern the ship was brought dangerously near to the ice barrier which at this point was higher than the rail of the ship. Those interested were granted the unusual spectacle of Polar animals looking *down* at them as the ship went past. A mighty bear walking over the ice stopped to push over a large boulder, hoping to find the lemmings who winter beneath it. The lemmings were out, probably being chased by the foxes who jump suddenly into the air and then crash dive through the ice, their tails pointing straight up – on top of the lemmings swimming furiously underneath the thin crust which forms between the crevices. Dead astern a number of walrus were asleep on drifting ice floes. Others were huddled together on the edge of the barrier, their skin frozen so hard that it would have been impossible to harm them – a harpoon, for instance, would have simply bounced off. Two walrus were standing in the water fast asleep, and a third was dozing upright with his tusks resting on an ice flow. *Arctic Fox* missed them by inches – and without waking them up. Some distance from the others another walrus dived to the bed of a rock shelf where he churned up the mud with his ivory tusks. Using his fore flippers, he collected an armful of mud and began to return to the surface. On the way up he rubbed his fore flippers against each other, crushing the mollusc shells he had collected along with the mud and letting the broken pieces sink back into the sea. On reaching the surface, the walrus stood straight up in the water with the oyster-like flesh of the mollusc shells floating about him. Having looked around and given what could easily have passed for a grin, he swallowed the flesh from the shelled molluscs one at a time and then went to sleep. His dive and ascent, both timed on a stop watch, confirmed that *Arctic Fox* was in dangerously shallow water for a vessel with a draft of 29 ft.

The ship was eased in to $1\frac{1}{2}$ knots, but she soon lost headway and had to be rung on to 3 knots before the rudder would answer the helm. Even this slight alteration in the backward movement of the ship caused her stern to swing round and grind into the ice, which missed damaging her steering mechanism by the narrowest of margins. The Bosun was surprised to find sweat beading up on his forehead and his moist palms losing their grip on the spokes of the wheel.

The echo from the ship's stern as it struck the barrier caused one very large and very curious bear to raise his head and turn round. Having watched the ship for a number of minutes, the bear decided to look closer at this strange object floating along on the ice. He stepped quietly into the water and swam slowly across, followed by the beam of the bridge searchlight. Twice he came up for air, and to make sure the ship had not moved out of sight. He was clever enough to cover his black nose with a white paw when he lifted his head clear, to make his face look like any other piece of ice. Having checked up on his quarry, he sank back into the water without a sound and surprised everyone by coming up in a stagy manner in the centre of the searchlight beam where he blinked and rubbed his ear with assumed nonchalance. Having yawned, he swam slowly to the starboard scupper port, which he peered through before rolling over and showing his brilliant white underfur. He came back to the scupper and pushed his snout through the bars before finally turning away. He swam off without looking back, clutching between his great jaws half a pound of dripping which All Sorts had flung nervously down in front of him.

The dripping would help supplement the fifty seals the bear could be expected to eat in a year, always providing he managed to run faster than the Eskimo hunters. Although merciless hunters, the Eskimoes believe they may expose themselves to the anger of the bear's soul if it is not treated with proper respect. Presents must be hung up for the slaughtered animal, and much thought obviously goes into choosing them. A present of sole skin is thought to be acceptable, for bears 'walk so much'. The Eskimoes also credit the Polar bear with magical properties and some north European countries are not free from this influence. At the chemist in Tromsø one can still buy bottles of bear-bile, from the gall-bladder. Mixed with a small quantity of spirits of camphor it relieves stomach pains. It requires a certain degree of courage to swallow this volatile mixture, but it was conspicuously successful in relieving the symptoms resulting from eating three-week-old frozen meat – *and* All Sorts, 'Risotto with butter beans in gravy', a sure killer if one was at all under the weather!

Possibly, this particular bear welcomed his contact with humans. The male Polar bear is the greatest wanderer amongst the Arctic mammals and one of the loneliest creatures on earth. In his journeyings across the enormous ice fields of the Polar Sea he is likely to span most of the Arctic region within his own lifetime – always on the move, always drawn by the migration of the seals. And he is almost always alone. It is possible that this one bear could have crossed the 89th parallel and might have visited the North Pole. He is certain to have avoided contact with his own kind, and they in turn would shun his company. His companions would have been the fox and the raven. These three are often seen together on hunting trips. The bear leads, with the fox following along behind, until they reach a seals' blow-hole – when the fox lies down on the ice and lets the bear do the work. The raven hops around between the two, but is not as loyal as the fox. The raven usually has two or three bears under observation and flies from one to the other intent on seeing which of them is the first to find a seal. Hunting over, these three turn back across the immense ice-floes, with the bear – King of the Arctic – leading the way, followed at a respectful distance by his attendants.

With the aid of glasses it was possible to follow the bear's tracks for a short distance after he had regained the ice field, and soon he was joined by his attendant fox. The fox trotted alongside and attempted to sniff at the dripping held in his master's jaws. He was shouldered heavily aside (the bear weighed something in the region of 900 lb.) and rolled over in the snow. The last glimpse of these two lonely voyagers was of the bear standing on an ice-floe with the fox sitting at his side, floating quite fast to the south-west in search, no doubt, of the next prospect. On this occasion there was no raven.

This was the last wild animal *Arctic Fox* was to see this trip, and the only Polar bear the crew had ever seen from the deck of their ship close enough to study its features. One or two auks came to rest along the ship's rail waiting for something to eat. These were fed on sardines which they regarded as a great delicacy. Having gobbled up the fish they lubricated their bills with the olive oil and sharpened them on the edge of the tin before flying away, squawking their thanks. The Eskimoes in the extreme north of Greenland still use the skins of the auk for shirts. The practice of making bird shirts is certainly an old one, and gives employment to the old, toothless women who chew the newly-caught skins to clean them of unwanted fat before sewing them together. Another of their winter chores is to pluck the eider duck of its down. Buster had an eider down pillow which he had (or so he said) filled himself from ducks he had captured. He guarded this pillow with unnecessary zeal, as it was full of ticks and everyone kept as far away from it as possible!

CHAPTER TWENTY-THREE

The current that sweeps along the edge of the slowly moving ice field carries masses of drift wood, some of it frozen inside icebergs. Most of this accumulation is tree trunks polished smooth from years of riding in Arctic ice. Once, they stood green and tall along the rivers of Siberia. Then the spring current melted the ice and cut down everything in its path, hurling the trees into the sea where they remain a menace, particularly to battered, un-seaworthy trawlers trying to go astern in darkness and hurricane seas.

Judging by the noise from the outside of *Arctic Fox's* hull, she had collided with this lot with some force. Already, a tall, slender birch was lying across the boat deck, and an immense pine – as tall as the ship's mast – had been washed on to the quarter-deck along with a larch tree which frightened the life out of All Sorts when its tip lodged in the galley porthole and pushed him in the back. He took off like a rocket – and clung with hands and feet to the water pipe until talked into coming down by the Mate, who explained that sharks didn't inhabit these waters!

One unfortunate consequence of passing through this densely packed timber was that the ship lost yet another piece of her life-saving equipment. One of the two remaining twelve-man self-inflatable life rafts had been torn from its cradle and was now floating upside down with supplies falling out from under its orange canopy. As the ship was backing with the current the raft stayed alongside for a considerable time but it was impossible to retrieve anything from the sea, and finally the raft was given up. It was noted with sombre interest by the crew as they watched it disappear that it had turned to ice both *inside* and out after eleven minutes in the water. The temperature at this time was 25 degrees above the lowest surface temperature known on earth. (– 125 degrees Fahrenheit). In 1777 sixty ships were lost here owing to their hulls being run through by logs. The ships were then blown into line by the wind and crushed – all at the same moment – by the nut-cracker action of two opposing ice-floes. Buster happened to know this true story and lost no time in repeating it. As his voice rose and fell above the wind screaming outside and the ship was buffeted by the great blocks of timber striking the hull, All Sorts – still white and trembling – swooned completely away.

'And now,' said the Badger, turning to Buster, 'you can get in that fucking galley and cook the grub yourself. Sadistic bastard, you are.'

After half an hour of twisting, turning, winding through a

maze of ice-floes riding like white swans on a green sea, *Arctic Fox* turned with the ice barrier running parallel to her port rail. She bounced and shuddered against a submerged iceberg before running clear, and then, suddenly, the sea was empty, and she was free to come round and back on her ground. This time she was going to shape a course which would take her round in a shallow arc before coming up on the sounding she had chosen. She turned through 125 degrees, taking in a mile of ocean.

Arctic Fox took such heavy seas that her stern and boat-deck were buried for long intervals, and the after wheel-house was flooded to a depth of three feet. This, as it turned out, acted as compensating ballast for the flooding for'ard, and as a result the ship was noticeably easier to manage.

Slowly, imperceptibly, her head came round the compass, and the ship finally stood on her point. After a moment or two, she started her run up onto the sounding and all hands took up station on the deck. The Skipper lowered the bridge window on the lee side and leaned out, looking down at the swell and assessing the lateral drift as the wind came on to the beam. With faultless timing he gave his first command.

'Cod End outboard.'

And then . . . 'LET GO!'

Down went the Cod End, and over the side went the net. As the fore door was released, the port winch drum was made free of its brake and the warp run fast off the drum, following the door into the sea. With the fore-door away and already 10 fathoms down, the after-door plunged into the sea when both winch drums began paying out an equal length of warp. No power is required on the winch when shooting away, as the weight of the trawl takes the net to the bed of the ocean assisted by the trawler as it moves forward at slow ahead.

Despite the great difficulty in keeping the net clear of the screw, the trawl was successfully shot away after ten minutes. The noise of the wind made audible command impossible and both winchmen were temporarily blinded by ice freezing on their eyelids. The two buckets of boiling water rushed on deck to un-freeze the winch clutches were soon smuggled behind the winch to provide 'foot warmers' for the Badger, who stood with one boot in each bucket whenever he got the chance. The Whippit considered this a useful device and decided to try it for himself, the result being that he had to be dragged aft to the galley where it took some time to free his boots from the iron grip of two buckets of frozen water. As both his feet were by this time anaesthetised he refused to take off his boot stockings as he was certain his toes must have dropped off from frostbite. After a dram of rum, he hobbled off to his berth complaining that things always worked for the Badger and never worked for him! There was probably no truth in the rumour that he was noticed soon afterwards sitting up in his bunk counting his toes, but Buster thought it worth keeping alive and the Whippit's subsequent denial fell on deaf ears. The Badger's only comment was: 'The next time, he wants to put his head in a bucket and then he's sure not to do himself any harm.'

With the trawl shot away and three hours to go before hauling time, the three deckmen on watch were kept on the deck to axe the ice off the bridge top and superstructure while the remainder of the crew crowded on to the mess-deck and were soon making 'Cheese Whizzes' and other delicacies beloved by trawlermen. Buster flicked his pack of cards and leered pleasantly at anyone who passed, and the Badger reappeared with a conspiratorial air, smelling of rum. As the 'issue' rum was locked in the Skipper's cabin and the deckmen had none of their own, it looked as though the engineers were in for a nasty shock when they returned from pumping out the flooded forehold. This looked even more likely when the Whippit came swaying along the companion way and whispered hoarsely in Buster's ear. Buster jumped up, flung down his cards and left the mess-deck with the air of a man on an important mission. Between them, the Whippit and Buster took everything to pieces in the engineers' berths, including the deck panels and the entire bulkhead alongside the bunks. By the time they had finished, large sections of the inside of *Arctic Fox's* hull lay exposed, and Buster held the Whippit by the ankles whilst he burrowed down almost to the keel. The Customs men would have shuddered with disbelief had they been present to watch a couple of experts dismantling the inside of a ship – and what they discovered as a result. It was – as Buster was to remark later – just like Christmas. Cigars, cases of beer and six bottles of rum came to light amidst howls of laughter – silenced momentarily as the two lit their cigars and poured rum into half-pint tumblers. The Badger was soon back on the scene and being unable to find a glass, poured his rum into a tin labelled 'Milk for Infants – the Best there is'. With tears streaming down their cheeks they divided the loot between them and having put everything back exactly as they found it left the engineers' berths with a bottle of rum pushed down inside each thigh boot – and an expensive aroma following in their wake. Understandably, nothing more was seen of these three until hauling time, although Bill had a surprise when he came in off the deck and tried to get into his berth. Through the cigar smoke and rum fumes he found three figures hastily stacking loot into *his* bunk. It was safer, the Badger pointed out, in Bill's bunk, as the engineers would never suspect *him* of robbing them.

He was right. They didn't. They simply told the Badger *he* had done it. The Badger replied that he may *look* a villain but he wouldn't stoop as low as that. The engineers gave him a lingering, distrustful stare and turned to Buster. They got nowhere with him. He played his old game of getting them to tell him all about it in detail so that he could help them find the lousy bastards who had done it. Having succeeded in getting the engineers to argue and contradict one another he wandered off and left them to the Whippit. The Whippit was frank and honest. He admitted that he knew who the thieves were, but he couldn't name them because he hadn't got any proof. But, he added with great sincerity, if he did get proof he would personally expose them and thereby exonerate his two friends whom the engineers had unfairly accused. Faced with three such bare-faced and accomplished liars (all sucking peppermints) the engineers became truculent, and suddenly took hold of the Whippit and shook him violently. Taken on singly, either of them was fair game for the fast, hard-punching Whippit, but two at once was a different matter. He went down with the other two on top of him and was clearly getting the worst of it. The Badger moved back, and stood quite still with his hands loose at his sides.

'Leave him alone,' he said quietly. He casually brushed his ginger hair from his eyes and kicked away a box by his feet.

'One's enough.'

The engineers pounded the Whippit.

'Did you hear? Get off him!' The Badger pulled up the sleeves of his jersey and flicked away his cigarette before ambling over to the three on the floor. He stood looking down at them for a minute or two, and then spoke again – still without menace. 'If you two don't lay off I'll turn you both into cripples.' Said by anyone else on board such a threat would have sounded funny. But it didn't sound a bit funny the way the Badger said it. It was backed, for one thing, by 294 pounds of controlled muscle power.

'I'll give you one more chance – get off him.' In reply the engineers continued to bang the Whippit's head on the floor. Suddenly, the Badger went into action. His hands bit deep into the backs of the two men's necks and with no apparent effort he jerked them upright. Using his right hand he gripped one by the throat and lifted him more than a foot from the deck until the veins protruded and the man's face turned purple. His head went slowly back from the pressure of the Badger's thumb on the thyroid cartilage. The Badger's right hand released the man's throat at exactly the same instant as he brought his left fist up from near the deck, uncoiled his arm away from his body and then drove it across and up. It smashed into the ridge of bone between the engineer's eyes and he fell to the deck. The remaining engineer made a move to the door and safety, but he was wrenched back and brought round.

Seldom outside the world of boxing can it be said that a man is literally saved from mutilation by the bell, but the engineer was certainly saved by the ship's bell as it rang for all hands. *Arctic Fox* was deviating so far out of her direct course that the tow had been cut short and the ship brought round ready to haul the trawl. With the wind a'beam the trawler lay over until her rail disappeared beneath the sea, and every one of the twenty men aboard was thrown to the deck.

In the case of the men keeping watch below and sleeping in the top bunks, this meant falling a distance of 5 ft. 0 in. to the floor. One of them – Paddy – was greeted with jeers and laughter when he appeared on the deck wearing his life-jacket (upside down), clutching two cans of beer and a comic. Clenched between his teeth was a whistle attached to the life-jacket by a cord, and around his neck were three dozen contraceptives wrapped in waterproof paper. As he would have floated upside down had he jumped into the sea Buster advanced the theory that the contraceptives would have come in handy as buoyancy floats once they were blown up into balloons. As this would have still left Paddy with his head beneath the waves and his bottom above water level this hardly seemed worthwhile, and the whistle wouldn't be much use either.

'Not at all,' replied Buster, 'He could stick *that* up his arse.'

The sober truth was that any man would have been frozen into a grotesque shape before he struck the water, whichever way he wore his life-jacket. The latest life-jacket specified by the Board of Trade (compulsory for all British Shipping before 1970) is already standard equipment aboard deep water trawlers.*

It is already highly suspect, too. Colin and Wacker each tried one out last summer (1966) during a stop in the North Sea under flat o'calm conditions. Although the tapes had been correctly tied round the waist both men were suspended *beneath* their jackets after three minutes in the water. Wacker's, lifting on a back wave, worked itself up until it slipped over his head, leaving him dangling beneath it.

These jackets are supposed to keep a man afloat indefinitely and, it is claimed, turn him over on to his back with his head above water, even when unconscious. It is doubtful if either of these claims could be proved effectively under Arctic conditions.

The temperature of the sea in these latitudes rarely exceeds 38 degrees, and on this occasion had dropped to a record low of

*It is currently reported (1967) that two trawlermen have been found dead in the Channel, each wearing one of these jackets which had slipped over their heads. Both bodies had throat abrasions consistent with strangulation, their only injuries. The sea was calm at the time. It was June.

34 degrees – just 2 degrees above freezing point. To breathe the air without covering the mouth with a muffler folded to provide maximum thickness would result in ice being drawn into the lungs and death would follow. Arctic survival clothing is useless on a trawler because it restricts rapid movement when speed and agility are demanded of the crew – namely, at hauling time. Similarly, life-saving equipment which leaves men exposed to the air prolongs life long enough for the lungs to freeze and the would-be survivors to be covered with layers of ice which builds up into a glass tomb with the people in it visible from the outside – some still erect, or frozen in suspended animation with their hands outstretched. In this macabre fashion they are likely to stay afloat and drift about the ocean – preserved inside the ice until it drifts into warmer latitudes or is spotted by a passing ship. Open wooden life-boats are more likely to cause this than the rubber air-filled life-rafts, but even inside these survival time is not likely to be more than a few hours if the crew abandon ship without the chance to grab adequate clothing. Protected by the canopy of the raft and suitably clad they may drift about long enough to be picked up, but only if they are sighted on the Radar screen of a trawler near enough to reach them in time. The recommended method of attracting a ship's Radar from a life-raft is to open the tins of fresh water from amongst the provisions and then bend the tins inside out so that they serve as reflector. Having opened enough tins, these are then tied together and hoisted to the top of the canopy where they are supposed to reflect back the electrical impulses transmitted by the ship sending them. As this utterly useless method necessitates getting rid of the drinking water to attract attention, would-be survivors are faced with the alternatives of freezing to death with no hope of rescue or dying of thirst in the belief that they would have been picked up if only they'd lived longer. There isn't a marine Radar in existence able to pick up half a dozen tin cans floating in rough seas – not even ten feet away. Fortunately, fishermen do not think about such things and regard the 'Survivors' Handbook' in the same light as they regard 'Beano' and 'Dandy' – good for a laugh but not to be taken seriously.

The logs, however, had to be taken seriously. There was enough timber – poles, planks and fully-grown trees – lying around the decks to build substantial winter quarters for the entire crew. A number of pit props, presumably from the coal mines on Spitsbergen, were rolling off the whaleback and bouncing down onto the foredeck where they wedged themselves into the fish pounds or jammed across the bollards (used as warp guides, and for paying out and hauling in the trawl). These pit props were easy to manhandle and cast back into the sea, but the tree trunks proved a great difficulty. Both the pines had to be sawn up into manageable pieces, and the larch needed eight men to get it back over the side. This must have been one of the few occasions when the deckhands on a trawler heard themselves addressed as 'the Fore and Aft log party'. Guided by the magnetic light of the Mate's personal presence the crew sawed and heaved until all obstructions were removed. The Mate positively enjoyed himself, and even roared with laughter when the Badger shouted to the rest of the crew to remember that the object in the yellow sou'wester was the Mate, who was not to be dumped with the other blocks of wood as there were too many witnesses about.

The crew's spirits had never been higher than at this moment, and soon they were to soar and keep on soaring. *Arctic Fox* was about to haul, and in the few remaining days left before she turned for home she was to make trawling history. History not of the kind to stir much interest amongst the public used to watching fish finger 'ads' on the telly, but of the kind that would make her name remembered for a long time to come amongst the group of hard core professionals who trawl the Arctic waters. Many trawlers could not have got this far without breaking up, or having done so would have been forced to turn back without shooting away. *Arctic Fox*, damaged and unseaworthy as she was, had penetrated an open icefield in mid Arctic winter less than 26 miles from the southern tip of Spitsbergen, and she had succeeded in getting her gear down for two hours and eighteen minutes. And now there was every sign that she had made a great haul of fish.

It is tempting to question the motives for such reckless behaviour, and many will no doubt do so. But amongst skippers and crews who earn their living under the existing system of payment there can be only one criterion – success. For the Arctic trawlerman, it remains nature's sweetest anodyne.

CHAPTER TWENTY-FOUR

There was no horizon, and the sea ran in a confused swell. The searchlight on the bridge top came on, followed by the 20 in. diameter searchlight on the foremast platform. The derrick lights and those along the casing flooded the pounds and the deck as far back as the after gallows. The sea danced in and out of the beams, and the Mollies flickered across for an instant before gliding into the night. The alcohol in the deck thermometer stood at a record low of minus 82 degrees Fahrenheit. Wacker stopped to look at it, and he froze. Both boots stuck to the deck and one heavily gloved hand became attached to the thermometer case and required a tap with a spanner before it was free again.

During towing both winch drums had been de-clutched and the brakes pinched up. Now they were back in clutch, with the 350 H.P. motor on full power bringing the trawl back to the surface at a rate of 310 feet per minute. The Cod End literally shot out of the water due to the buoyancy caused by the expansion of the air in the bladders of the fish. *Arctic Fox* went astern to bring the net farther along the side of the ship, and the manual hauling of the net – hand over hand – began. The vastly swollen Cod End was dragged closer to the side of the ship until it was near enough to be encircled by the bag becket and lifted clear of the sea by the fore Gilson. Not even *Arctic Fox's* lifting gear was adequate to bring the catch inboard in one operation, and the bag was divided in two. By the time the Cod End had been emptied for the second time the pounds were waist deep in 4 tons of fish! The bulk of the catch was made up of cod weighing from 200 lb. down to 10 lb. In addition, there was a 434 lb. halibut, a ray with a 7 ft. 0 in. wing span and a number of fully grown hake.

Hake were not previously considered to exist in these waters as they prefer muddy ground, not favoured by the cod, and eat mostly shrimps. There was an unusually large number of catfish (Anarhichas lupus). These sea reptiles were all over 4 ft. 0 in. long and weighed around 50 lb. each. Their large heads contain very powerful teeth, pointed and wedge-shaped, to enable them to grip with the front of their mouths, and thick and rounded at the back of the jaws for grinding hard shells, spider crabs and mollusc. The strong, tough skin makes excellent leather and is occasionally used by fishermen for book covers. Being uneatable and therefore unsaleable they are thrown back into the sea before gutting starts, but numbers of them remain buried under other fish and are not revealed until later.

Buster knew this as well as anyone and had already gone for'ard in search of his liver basket. Buried beneath the sea fans, dead men's fingers and the beautiful sea corallines was an Arctic salmon. This fish (5 ft. 0 in. long) had a date tag behind its gill which showed that to reach its point of capture it had travelled 25 miles a day. It was most probably making for the less saline waters farther south, guided by the pattern of polarised light produced in the sea by an oblique sun or moon, emitting rays invisible to the human eye. This prize was handed to All Sorts who would score the fish along it flanks and then rub in a mixture of ground black pepper, nutmeg and mace before steaming it in a shallow dish. Another of All Sorts' dishes the crew could now expect was made from cods' hearts, cut out whilst still palpitating and thrown into a pot of boiling water scented with basil and rosemary. The taste was like jugged pheasant. His alternative method was to bake them in batter. The cheek muscles, too, were good to eat when baked.

With well over 3,000 fish in the pounds, gutting started immediately. With the gutting knife held in the right hand the deckmen cut the nape of the fish from left to right, opened the belly by a quick downward thrust, removed entrails and saved the liver. Each man could be expected to gut a fish of any weight and size every 10 to 15 seconds. With the Bosun in charge of gutting on the deck, the Mate disappeared down the hatch into the fishroom to supervise the stowing of the catch. The fishroom had a capacity of 16,000 cubic feet. All interior fittings were removable to facilitate stowing, cleaning and discharging fish. Battens and the light alloy sheathing used as shelves were made from aluminium to prevent contamination of the fish by germs. Wood collects bacteria and was used only to make up partitions. The fish hold was broken up by upright partitions and staging laid horizontally and referred to as shelf pounds. Beneath the staging were the underfoots, and aft were the bulk pounds for the less valuable fish such as coalie, cats and monk. Headroom was limited to five feet, and the 80 tons of crushed ice used during the ten days of fishing had to be cracked at a speed and under conditions which would have appalled a coal miner.

With the ship heeling, the floor thick with slime and an open drop of 10 ft. 0 in. on three sides, ice breaking calls for muscle and agility. Wacker had both, and he also happened to be the shortest man aboard. For trip after trip, protesting and mutinous, he found himself in the fishroom – where he sang at the top of his voice and muttered 'fucking bastard job this is' at the end of every refrain. As the fish from the deck piled up on the staging, the Mate stowed the catch. It was laid one fish deep on each shelf, belly down, head outward, tail fin centre; with ice beneath it but not along its back. As the singing floated up the shelves filled to the deckhead and the tally of fish began to rise. When it comes to understanding the tally it is necessary to be extremely knowledgeable to follow the calculations at all. The haul from the cod end is estimated in 'baskets' (1 basket is three-fifths of a kit). In the fishroom, the catch is stowed not in baskets but on staging, where it is reckoned up in 'kits'. (A kit is ten stone). Only livers are kept in baskets, and these are rendered down on board ship and estimated by the gallon. As if this obtuse regard for the weights and measures in use elsewhere were not enough, the crew's cash return for the fish sold is called poundage. This has nothing to do with the weight of fish caught, but relates to the price it fetches on the day it is sold. Included in the poundage payment is the crew's share of the liver oil, which is worked out at a fixed price per gallon.

Arctic Fox's tally broke her previous record for a single haul and established a new one for a United Kingdom trawler operating in an area never before penetrated by a fishing vessel in high Arctic winter. She had paid the price, and would continue to do so, but she was at last catching fish in enough quantity to justify the great risks she had taken. If she avoided being crushed, didn't go down or break up before she turned for home, her feat would be even more remarkable.

The Skipper decided to risk a call to *Arctic Fox's* sister ship and give her the news in as guarded terms as possible. Owing to the distance separating the ships it was doubtful if she would pick up the call or be heard in reply if she did. The Sparks made 3 ten-second calls but failed to get an answer. Suddenly a voice was heard, faint but clear, struggling through the atmospherics. It was Mac the Bastard's voice.

'Well, Well, Well, so that's where you are! Are you on 'em? Filling your boots? Can – you – hear – me – *Arctic Fox*? Are you swagging it?'

Arctic Fox's skipper's astonishment overcame his caution.

'Yes, we've found 'em!'

'Keep 'em to yourself then – and Good Luck – you deserve it.'

It was possible to believe that by concentrating on the loud-speaker Mac's restless eyes and inquisitive nose – set in a face whose ugliness semed to mock at itself – would appear. But the voice was real enough. He would be sitting in the radio room on his canary-coloured trawler ceaselessly fidgeting – opening an endless succession of beer cans with one hand whilst he picked his nose with the other. From this favoured position he had mastered plots and counter-plots; misdirected his enemies with every kind of duplicity and double dealing, tacking about so well and so often that friend and foe united in sheer self defence. And then, when he had grabbed his share of fish and turned for home, he would settle himself before the transmitter and talk. Talk in which opinions, vitriolic abuse, obscure jokes and blistering remarks were strangely blended with brilliant shafts of seafaring knowledge. He castigated skippers he didn't like and had never seen. Poured scorn on fast ships he had (somehow) managed to overtake, and ordered those ahead to get out of his way. He had one virtue which cancelled out every one of his many faults. He was incapable of being jealous. If someone caught fish after a run of bad luck or misfortune he was the first (and often the only one) to wish them well, usually in incredibly fast morse which he sent himself, with one hand on the key and the other hand opening the beer. It was impossible to say where he was at this moment, but wherever he was he was certain to have his decks swamping with fish and his crew singing at the tops of their voices. Nets, rope, warp wires, bridles, floats and bobbins would be festooning the ship from one end to the other and his cabin would be stacked to the deck head with rum and cases of beer. The tiny patch of carpet left to walk on would be covered with charts and littered with books. The rack alongside his bunk would be stuffed with 'urgent' unopened messages from the ship's owners and his false teeth would be in the compass binnacle wrapped in the *Trawling Times*. He was the most predictable and the most exasperating man to have any dealings with and, of course, he was widely detested. Someone remarked that Mac had succeeded in earning the respect of his enemies and the hatred of his friends – and as he treated everyone alike no one knew for sure which side they were really on. Possibly the ship's owners were in the same dilemma. Because of his undoubted success they grudgingly overlooked his many transgressions, but saw as little of him as they could. He held the distinction of never being invited anywhere by anyone and inflamed those who had so carefully avoided him by thanking them for not having intruded on the few free hours he spent ashore. His greatest distinction was one he most likely remained unaware of – or remembered only as a piece of sarcasm. The Badger, on his first trip to sea, had addressed Mac the Bastard as 'Sir'. It was probably the first and only time he had been addressed in so formal a term, although he had used it himself on one occasion. It was the day on which the late King had, at a special investiture, decorated Mac with the D.S.M. – for bravery during minesweeping operations on a trawler. Shaved, sober and suited, with squeaky orange boots, Mac must have presented a proud, if unusual, picture, and the one regret must be that no one bothered to take the old warrior's photograph.

The storm was abating and conditions for trawling were noticeably more favourable. This was evident from the speed the ship was now making through the water. Due to a sudden and unexpected change in the direction of the wind, *Arctic Fox* was obliged to steam back to the start line before shooting away. She would not have found it necessary to adopt this time-wasting procedure had she been able to find bottom where she was by using the sounder. As the sounder was unreliable the Skipper wisely decided to go back the way he had come and follow the exact line of the previous tow. This entailed turning the ship's head *away* from the storm. The danger from a following sea is greatest when the waves rolling along behind travel at the same speed as the ship itself. The safest method is to 'run before' by increasing speed and thereby out-distancing them. But in allowing a vessel of the size of the *Arctic Fox* to turn in a gale blowing from behind, speed had to be reduced for reasons of safety. In accepting this loss of speed in the sixty seconds it would take to bring the ship round, the Skipper was gambling against the moment of greatest danger. There was no alternative if the crew were to be kept earning money, but many a trawler has been lost in the seconds it takes to carry out the turn. Everyone aboard knew to some degree what was entailed, and the ship's Captain was suddenly the least envied man aboard.

The ship eased in to the turn. The track of the wake began its curve as the wheel went over and the rudder answered. It looked as though she was safely round! Then, without warning, the ship was struck with great violence by a breaking wave from the following sea which buried the foredeck level with the rail. The head trim of the ship – already aggravated by internal flooding – increased. The breaking waves from astern and on both sides flooded the foredeck to the top of the bulwarks and the whole of the forepart of the ship disappeared under the sea. At this moment the stern clawed the sky and the rudder refused the helm. Immediately the first breaker struck, the ship stopped her engine (a faultless piece of timing by the Skipper) and she turned to bring her stern straight against the sea. She was kept there by violent and constant manoeuvre of rudder and propeller. If her stern moved from this position by more than 36 in. the ship would be turned across the sea by the orbital motion of the waves striking obliquely across her stern and she would roll over. The weight of water from the next wave deposited 131 tons of sea down on to the ship and it was obvious that stability and buoyancy were exhausted to a point where she would capsize and sink. Other breaking waves were coming in at a speed of 19 ft. 0 in. per second in a traverse thrust along the port side.

With so much head trim she was certain to be turned across the sea by the stern breakers. To order abandon ship would be tantamount to sending every man to his death, and the only safe moment had passed minutes before. It was now a matter of holding on with an iron grip to avoid being knocked unconscious – and wait. Another wave struck before she regained her centre of gravity and the ship veered across the crest and fell down sideways into the trough. For a moment or two she stayed in the position into which she had been thrown, waiting for just one more blow. The blow that would kill her.

Technically she should have gone down already. Having fallen into the trough sideways on and been struck by a wave on the windward side when already far inclined the other way, her centre of buoyancy had moved towards the side the wave struck. In technical terms, 'the static capsizing moment had been created'. She must have been beneath the sea along her entire length at one moment – but still she stayed afloat. The armour-plated glass windows fronting the bridge burst into fragments and the sea roared in, leaving the ship's bell to crash down on to the winch. Ratlines were carried away and the forepeak rails twisted into knots before disappearing into the sea. And the last piece of life-saving equipment had gone. Pound boards were reduced to matchwood and the stern rails crushed flat. Foam boiled half way up the funnel and the sea roared down the companion ways carrying supplies and gear with it.

In trying to recover from this desperate situation the ship

139

reduced her speed so much that she was literally hove to by the stern before being seized by the head and forced back against the thrust of her propeller. With the bridge windows knocked out it was impossible to judge what the ship was doing or where she stood in relation to the sea but three men still held the wheel and the engine room gave instant effect to their orders.

The ship, however, was completely out of control. The Siemens indicator showed the angle of the ship's rudder at hard a starboard, with the ship's head going in the same direction instead of hard a port.

'We've lost her!' yelled the Skipper. 'We can't hold her now ... she's rolling over ... nearly on her side. Paddy! Right the helm! Ken? Ken! Stand by to ring her on full ... when I say. We *must* catch her when she's got centre buoyancy and her head's pointing up – NOW!! NOW!! Full Ahead!!'

The Mate flung the handle down and stood with his arms locked against the pedestal. The ship's screw began to answer at the same instant as her bow showed high and clear against the sky. *Arctic Fox* shuddered, faltered, and careened – but she did not fall back, and with one last heave she stood with her head against the waves.

The water poured off the decks and rushed back into the sea through the scupper ports, leaving the superstructure glistening with beads of salt and crystals of ice frozen into surrealist patterns by the wind. Although the solid water had run off without forming ice, the spray had frozen the moment it struck and all raised features now resembled icebergs. At its highest reach the spray had lapped the foremast and left jagged spurs of white crystal hanging from the wooden truck at the head of the topmast which stood thirty feet above deck level. The interior bulkheads of the ship had also iced up due to the sea forcing open the doors of the booby hatch which had collapsed, blocking the only exit to the lifeboat deck. It was impossible to say why and how *Arctic Fox* had survived this savage beating, but she had.

140

CHAPTER TWENTY-FIVE

Reaction throughout the ship had differed widely and gave rise to stories both apocryphal and true: Buster, knocked flat and unable to rise, quietly packing anything within his reach into a seabag. All Sorts skidding back and forth across the galley, kneeling on a prayer mat with his hands raised in supplication. Harry flung from a lower bunk to the floor and then thrown upwards again until he landed on Colin clinging to a topside bunk – who in turn fell out and into a fire bucket. The engineer lifted forcibly off the lavatory by a vertical column of water and then thrust back again until he jammed in the seat. The Badger wearing a life-jacket floating horizontally up and down the port gangway with an expression of sublime indifference, holding a glass jar to his chest. The Whippit flung 15 ft. 0 in. and landing upside down still clutching a water-logged sandwich. And Bill, who was thrown with great violence into the spud locker and remained locked in until long after *Arctic Fox* had recovered.

It was impossible to say that any of these 'survivors' had been infected by the real dangers of the situation, even though they were aware of them, and personal discomfort claimed more concern than the fact of their survival.

The Skipper, Ken and Paddy, in their struggle to control *Arctic Fox*, were stunned, soaked and exhausted, and were quite unable to speak for some while after. They, at least, gave thanks to the relenting ocean, but only one crewman made any reference to the incident – and that was an oblique one. Barry had been last off the deck and found the half door on the quarter-deck secured against him. He ran for the liver room and wedged himself just as *Arctic Fox* reached the second degree of her turn. He had escaped serious injury by sitting inside the empty liver boiler and was now feeling oily and unusually talkative. 'Ah were bummled about like a bee in a bottle. Ma 'ands are clumpst with cold and ma beeats is all clag'd wid oil and ah'm fair clagg'd too. Ah were left standing in the bleak 'cause the weather door was shut.'

'We thought you'd gone home,' commented the Whippit.

'Shut oop, Whippit, Ah'll be clouten thee else. Ah'm joost in thar raight mood.'

He looked it, too, and after a pot of tea he oiled his way to his berth and banged the door.

'He's the only trawlerman I know,' mused the Badger, 'who spells shovel c-h-u-v-e-l.'

'Maybe he's right,' replied Buster, keeping a straight face.

'How would you know? You've no idea what a shovel looks like, you whiffling old bastard.'

The fact that she was still afloat and able to continue fishing shortly after was high praise for *Arctic Fox's* designers and proof that a skipper with an instinctive feeling for his ship could prevent her loss providing he could make his intentions clear to others in time.*

Understandably, he was given a rousing cheer when he appeared to inspect the damage. His only comment: 'Well, that's what Mac the Bastard would have done, I feel sure.' No time was lost in repairing the worst of the damage and everyone was surprised to find that a bare six minutes had elapsed since the first wave had struck. The bilge pumps would contain the leaks and the ship was otherwise watertight at deck level. There were no

---

* Note to trawler designers: Notwithstanding this fully justified conclusion, had the traverse metacentric height of this vessel been raised from the existing 1.6 ft. (at departure) to something in the region of 2.8 ft., many of her difficulties in rough seas would have been resolved and her imminent capsize averted altogether. This alteration would not have seriously affected the ship's rolling period and would satisfy the persistent and unavailing pleas of deep water skippers for an increase in the G.M. for vessels of this class. The increase would further allow for a safety margin great enough to withstand the heeling moments of the trawl warps at hauling time. It would seem that many of the recommendations of naval architects stem originally from pure assumptions, the validity of which has to be proved or disproved empirically at the risk of men's lives. Designers should question these 'assumptions' before accepting them, and pay far more attention to the Tank Testing facilities available – particularly those tests relative to small craft in a following sea. If this information were considered alongside advice from deep water skippers the result would lead to increased safety, and take designers away from the realms of conjecture and theory based on blueprint formulas and closer to the actual requirements of the men employed to handle the ships they design.

injuries amongst the crew, apart from bruising, and the deckies had recovered sufficiently to ask for an extra dram of rum. The Skipper issued two bottles, and Wacker acted as Grog Kid.

And so, with renewed fire in their bellies, the crew assembled back on deck and *Arctic Fox* shot away a mile from where she last hauled. Although there were few signs for the experienced eye to read, there was one reliable indication that *Arctic Fox* would repeat her record haul of fish. The blue colour of the deep ocean is caused by the breaking up of water molecules. The less of other material there is in the sea the bluer it appears. The blueness in the ocean is a sign of barrenness and lack of pasturage, with few minute animals and no plant life. Conspicuous green is due to the presence of water soluble substances and an abundance of calcareous matter such as coralline. These, together with plankton, provide the staple food of the cod fish.

Illuminated by the beam of the searchlight the Arctic Ocean was apple green near the surface and dark olive below. 'We can't fail to catch 'em,' said the Skipper. With the trawl over the side, speed was reduced to 4 knots. Immediately, *Arctic Fox* slammed her bow down into the sea with tremendous force. There was little doubt that her head trim had increased and there was now a permanent list of 9 degrees to starboard. This reduced the low freeboard still further and the high waves buried the deck along its entire length. Green sea poured over the bulwarks as she lay over and she was noticeably slow to recover. Calculations made with the aid of drawings of the ship showed the weight of water taken inboard to be 128 tons on a single fully-developed wave. Although the stern profile was well raked aft above the waterline with adequate deadline in the sections of the run, it too disappeared from sight as the sea travelled aft. The propeller, immersed $4\frac{1}{2}$ ft. under water, leapt 10 ft. into the air, followed by the stern crashing back into the sea in a cloud of atomised spray and small splinters of wood. These splinters were from the stanchion on which the rudder was hung. It was thought prudent to find out if any other ship was in range, but no reply was made to *Arctic Fox's* radio call and the Radar was clear of everything but ice for sixty miles. It transpired later that she was more than

90 miles from the nearest ship (a Russian ice breaker working out of Murmansk). Sixty miles was the limit of *Arctic Fox* high definition Radar.

It also became known afterwards that the Russians had carefully noted *Arctic Fox's* bearing and checked her position on the charts. Regular watch was kept on the radio frequency she had used and a time of 15 hours 10 minutes estimated as the least time required to cover the distance separating the two ships. There was some surprise on board the ice breaker when they finally realised where *Arctic Fox* was, and they were dumb-founded when it was subsequently discovered that *Arctic Fox* displaced 1,000 tons and measured a mere 200 ft. overall. A few days later *Arctic Fox* made radio contact with the ice breaker and was greeted with a bright, 'Hello. Good Morning. How are you?' from the Russian girl operator who spoke good English and was obviously pleased to be given the chance to use it.

'Would you,' she enquired, 'like the news from the Soviet mainland relayed in English?'

'Yes,' *Arctic Fox* replied.

'Only the atmospherics are distorted, not the news,' the girl added with a gay laugh.

The Soviet English-language broadcast was relayed throughout the ship, and reception was remarkable. Equally surprising was the speed with which the various recordings used had been monitored from the BBC transmitter. Demonstrations made by nuclear disarmament groups in Trafalgar Square and Downing Street four hours earlier were clearly heard.

CHAPTER TWENTY-SIX

In common with most distant-water trawlers *Arctic Fox* was equipped with all the modern electronic devices she was ever likely to need. She had, amongst other things, a meter for measuring the direction and speed of water currents; an automatic marine log; a navigational echo sounder; a cathode ray fish de-

tector; a high definition radar, and a compass which in Columbus'
day might have been thought of as mildly progressive.

All these instruments had failed at some time during the trip,
and now it was the compass's turn. The compass consisted of a
card, using a balanced needle suspended at its centre and
magnetized at one end. It was suitably calibrated to counteract
the iron surrounding it by soft iron in the binnacle itself which
provided the housing. An instrument so simple can hardly go
wrong, except for one thing. Near the Pole the horizontal magnetic field falls below 0.05 gauss (the limit of sensitivity), whilst
the vertical field is powerful enough to destroy accurate reading –
and it is the horizontal field from which a ship takes its direc-
tional reading. For the time being the ship was lost on the high
seas. There was no sun to shoot, no stars. No land to provide a
cross bearing. No speed constant to give a D.R. position. Nothing
anywhere to give an accurate fix. It wasn't even possible to
place the ship's head by the compass any longer. She might – for
all anyone knew – have made up her own mind, and be steaming
to Russia – and captivity.

Arctic Fox steered as best she could by Radar, and the crew
interested itself in other, more urgent, matters. On the mess-deck
Buster was trying on a snow shoe Harry had made out of the
Sparks' squash racquet. The need for snow shoes was, in Harry's
view, imminent.

Owing to *Arctic Fox's* great draught the rudder extended a
very short distance from the stern post and little of it could be
seen from the stern rails. If it collapsed, one very uncertain
possibility remained open. The wind and sea would drive the
ship close to the limits of the ice and crash her against the barrier
where she would sheer off against the impact before being thrown
back. In those few seconds the crew would have their only
chance to jump over the side, down on to the ice. From there they
could walk to the small island at the tip of the Spitsbergen
archipelago. Once the ice-free ridge at South Cape was reached
they would have to swim to the mountainous perimeter of the
island. Providing, of course, they got that far. Crevices and wide
breaks in the field itself would take a long time to cross in

darkness and the direct route of twenty-four miles harboured deep fissures hidden under thin layers of snow. The island promised nothing – there was no shelter – and it would give nothing. The relentless forces of nature would either turn the survivors to ice or claw them back into the sea.

With night glasses it was possible to look across in the direction of South Cape. Beyond the open field the ice lay unbroken all the way to the horizon, but a mile before South Cape it would be piled up in blue, jagged heaps, groaning and riding up against the submerged rocks. At the foot of the island the shore would be built high with irregular shifting masses of ice and frozen spray. The wind from the Polar cap would be less intense than on the open sea, but strong enough to fling the powdered snow into the air and against the deep scars in the rock face. All around would be a world terrifying in its level whiteness, and the night would be loud with the crying wind. Beneath a dense black sky heavy with snow and lit with a single star of emerald blue, the ice vapour would be falling from above into the glacier filled valleys.

Man could not possibly live there. Birds were dying, even near the ship. A white Arctic falcon fell exhausted on to the bridge top.

It would not again endure the months of darkness and cold, waiting for the spring. It had died, like most of its kind, from cold. Clinging to its already frozen feathers were the dried leaves of wild Betony and Crowberry, all that remained of its winter nest. It was gathered up with strange gentleness by Colin, and carried to the ice-encrusted rail of the ship. He lingered there for a while before climbing to the boat deck and along to the stern. He cast the falcon into the boiling sea and watched it float away. When asked later why he had not thrown the dead bird over the side, he replied: 'Because I didn't want it harmed by the propeller.'

The only other place accessible from the sea and likely to provide shelter was Olsokbreen on the archipelago itself. This could only be reached by a suitable protected lifeboat and *Arctic Fox* had, of course, lost the two she normally carried. Bears

146

winter at Olsokbreen, and there was at least one log hut used by seal trappers in the summer.

The dramatic possibilities inherent in this new situation were as food and drink to Buster. Here at last was an unassailable true story with every chance of a perilous ending. No one knew whether the rudder would hold out and Buster thought it best to give one or two selected clients his 'candid appraisal' of what they could expect if it didn't. He clutched his way to the galley and button-holed All Sorts. He spoke of wild huskies, ravenous wolves and man-hugging bears; walruses who impaled men on their tusks and left them to die alone on the ice, and great seals who crushed men's skulls with one blow from their flippers. There was no hope, Buster implied, of escaping them all, and All Sorts' chances were candidly slim because he was not used to being exposed to the weather and his flat feet prevented him running fast enough. At this moment, Buster was joined by the Badger and his cronies whose approach to the crisis was severely practical. They had plans for building a sledge to carry the ship's rum (food wasn't mentioned), which All Sorts was to help drag across the ice whilst the rest of the party drove off the wild animals. The journey, said the Badger in his grandest manner, would be terrible, and only his party stood any chance of reaching land. If All Sorts wanted to join this privileged group he would have to help in the preparations. 'Your job, All Sorts,' said the Badger, clamping his great fist down on the cook's shoulder, 'is to build the sledge'. But All Sorts didn't want to go. He repeated Buster's 'candid appraisal' and mentioned the hazards. All these seemed trivial when compared with the Badger's graphic account of the fate awaiting those who failed to get off the ship in time. Helped by short, dramatic sentences, whispered close to his ear, All Sorts was made to see the stark horror of it all. The great rudder wrenched from its post, followed by the sound of splintering wood as the stern collapsed into the sea and the ship turned across the waves and filled with icy water. And there were only a few life-jackets left and All Sorts couldn't swim! But All Sorts was more afraid of the man-hugging bears which Buster told him would be lying in wait. 'All you need for them,' said the Badger, reassuringly, 'is a pot of honey at the end of a long pole. Then when they come at you, you push the honey in front of 'em. Bound to work – they *love* honey.'

'I haven't *got* any honey.'

'Then I'll trade you some for a few drams of rum, but only after you've made the sledge.'

'Where do I find the wood?'

'Saw yer bunk up.'

All Sorts hurried to his berth and closed the door.

The Chief Engineer came on to the bridge and found the Skipper standing in the voice position on the starboard forward corner of the bridge.

'Well, Skip, I've made an inspection. The rudder's taken a hell of a knock and I can't be sure it'll last until we get in. It's reduced speed all the way from now on, at any rate.'

'Who said so?'

'Well, she won't stand much more of this weather. Er, I was going to suggest we put in somewhere – just for inspection, like. The Russian coast isn't too far off, is it?'

'They won't allow us in unless we're badly iced up, and they won't give us a berth. Just tell us to drop the hook inside the harbour and watch us till we leave.'

'But under the circumstances . . .'

'*They're* not to blame for our circumstances, are they?'

The Skipper wedged himself more securely into the corner of the bridge, legs braced against the incessant pitching and rolling, eyes narrowed to defensive slits as the fragments of another bow wave flew into his face through the broken windows.

'Get someone to fix the windows.'

Otherwise he ignored the alert expressions of those about him and turned back to look out at the desolate waste of the inhospitable sea. Once or twice he moved quickly back to dodge the frozen spray sweeping into the open bridge, but for some minutes he said nothing.

'We're here to catch fish, Chief. Everything else is secondary.'

'That's your last word, is it?'

'I hope not,' said the Skipper with a strong touch of irony.

'Supposing the steering packs up, what then?'

The Skipper shrugged. There was an answer to that one, one that didn't have to be spelt out. He was too familiar with danger to show any fear – they all were, the Chief included. At sea one accepted the possibility as the crew accepted discomfort, soaking wet clothes, tiredness. These were all part of the job.

The Chief would go straight to the Gaffers when they got back – *if* they got back – but that didn't matter, providing they caught fish. A skipper's only as good as his last trip. *His* last trip had been a failure, and so had the one before that. But this one might be a success – there was every indication it would be. There were dozens of reasons, apart from the rudder, why he should call the whole thing off and make for the nearest harbour, but they all added up to something he couldn't accept.

'The steering will last out,' he said quietly. 'I'll take the responsibility.'

'It happens to be *my* responsibility.'

'It was, until just now. Now it's mine.'

'Being responsible for it won't do it any good if it suddenly decides to pack up.'

'It *won't*.'

The austere emphasis of the remark made the Chief flinch. There would be an inquest the minute he arrived back in the engine room and he would doubtless blurt out what he would say to the Gaffers. The Sparks would keep his ears open on the messdeck and carry the gossip back to the bridge. There were some silent mealtimes ahead in the officers' cabin.

CHAPTER TWENTY-SEVEN

That day breakfast and dinner were very silent indeed. Everyone was tired, which didn't help much. They'd been tired before – too tired to eat sometimes – but some common topic had usually roused them. Now, they just sat. The Captain. The Mate. The Chief Engineer. The Class II Radio Officer (with his own ivory-handled knife and fork). The Bosun. All picked at the plain but appetizing food – and said nothing.

Working on the deck or the bridge, they needed only a few gestures, a word here and there, to convey their meaning, whilst at other times they were moved by the same love and contempt for the job they knew so well. Perfunctory as it so often was, talking brought them together. Fishing prospects alone were good for twenty minutes. No one mentioned them at all now. Their silence isolated them as though each man knew there was nothing left they could discuss impersonally. The odd remark drifted into exile. Innocent questions melted on the air. A particularly good joke crashed in noisy silence, as eyes strayed to watch the Skipper's reaction. Feeling the hostility they gave up and waited for the meal to end.

At tea time the Skipper sat in loneliness whilst the others sat across the table opposite him – hoping they could be silent together with safety. The situation was absurd. At best it was uncomfortable. It lasted, just the same. It lasted until the Skipper suddenly spoke. Quite casually, he leaned back and said: 'I hope you're not all *that* tired. In an hour or two we'll be making history.'

Turning at the door he enquired: 'Anyone seen our galley boy? That jam's growing a mould.'

Tightening his muffler, the Mate swore carefully, and picking up a fork he bent it in half.

The galley boy had been sea-sick for many days. Thrown from his bunk more times than he cared to remember, he'd taken to sleeping on the floor. This, he found, was worse than anything! He'd known for some time that the ship was going to sink and would have felt comforted if only someone had said so. He had seen for himself how the splinters of wood flew off as the stern lifted and crashed back into the sea, and wondered why no one seemed to care. They just watched the ship breaking up and then stumbled off without a word. Later, through the fog, shrouded and raw, a berg as large as the ship caressed the rail with icy fingers. Shimmering metallic blue like a flawless gem, it pushed the ship aside and came so close that he could hear the water running though the sub-glacial channels inside it.

He was afraid. Soon he was too ill to care and lay on the floor hoping to sleep. No one came to see if he was all right. Presumably he wasn't missed, or perhaps they knew and just didn't care about him any more. Suddenly, the ship rolled on her side and the sea came surging in and covered his face and then his body. The water was colder than he expected, and thick with oil. *Arctic Fox* was going to sink – he was sure of that. When he tried to stand his legs gave way and he screamed – but nobody could hear. Perhaps they were dead already. Perhaps they'd left him behind, forgotten he was there. He managed to crawl to the door and found it locked. Above the surge of the water in the gangway outside, he could hear voices.

'That's the last of the life-rafts away.'

'Ay. All the boats are gone now.'

He cried out: 'Don't leave me. Wait – I can't get out!'

After that the engine stopped, and burning oil billowed in under the door. The ship turned completely over. He knew it had turned over because in the darkness he flung out his hand and found he was clutching the ventilator cap in the deckhead. It was beside him, and it should have been high above his head. Could trawlers, he wondered, stay afloat upside down? He heard the telemotor cut in as the rudder fought to save the ship. Then it cut out, and the lighting dynamo whined to a stop. Suddenly the engine burst into life and then began to roar, and finally it screamed and went on screaming. The ship started to climb and climb and climb, and then it leaned forward and began to dive. This was the moment. He had seen it often on the films. Stricken ships tilting up before they plunged quickly to the bottom. He screamed, and clawed with his fingers at the bulkhead. He was going to die. He screamed again and the door opened inwards. He fell out and crawled along towards the afterdoor and then lost consciousness. The water filled his lungs and choking, he woke up and crawled on. Suddenly a large wave picked him up and flung him back, deep inside the ship. He felt his body grow stiff and his limbs harden. He believed he was already dead . . .

This was the story of misery and terror which unfolded as the galley boy lay ashen and trembling on the floor of the mess-deck with the crew standing round him. He was badly shocked and still too frightened to move, but he would recover.

'All I want,' he said, between sobs 'is to get off this bastard ship and never come back.'

'Finished with the sea, have you?' said Buster in a gruff, friendly voice.

'For ever,' came the slightly hysterical reply.

The Mate arrived just in time to hear the last remark and stayed to listen to the youth's story. He was visibly unmoved by the drama. He had never panicked like that. It took time – a long time – to gain experience and even experience counted for nothing in the long run. The Mate had sixteen years' experience behind him, knew it all – and then when he thought about it would admit he knew just enough to stay alive. One couldn't hope for more, but that was enough. The sea would grant you that, providing you didn't panic. She would grant you, strictly on her terms, the chance to stay alive.

The Mate explained this to the galley boy, and more besides. It came as a surprise to some to hear him expressing his feelings. It showed humanity.

'If you can say,' the Mate concluded, 'after just three trips that you're finished with the sea, the experience has been cheap at the price – very cheap. But don't change your mind later on, because the sea won't change.'

Turning to Buster : 'Get him to his berth. Make him eat apples and dry bread. Don't let him lie down, and take the key off him. And you lot needn't stand there like a lot of spare pricks at

152

a wedding – I'll soon find you a job if you've nothing else to do. It's about time we posted look-outs atop of the foremast . . .'

The crew vanished, only the Bosun remained.

'Barry,' said the Mate, turning to address him, 'I wanted a word with you. We may have another head case on our hands. I hear on the grapevine that All Sorts's taken to sleeping on the floor. Apparently he's sawn his bunk up to make some sort of toboggan. What do'ye think's behind that?'

Barry, surprisingly ill-informed, said he thought the cook had become very superstitious of late. This surmise, although wrong in its particular reference, was accurate enough in its wider implications. With three exceptions, the *whole* of *Arctic Fox's* crew was superstitious, and without exception they all denied it. And yet . . .

CHAPTER TWENTY-EIGHT

On this and previous trips Colin had discreetly stuck a gutting knife in the mast to bring luck, and when ashore refused to sharpen one after sunset. Minutes before talking to Barry the Mate had recalled with evident approval the fact that *Arctic Fox* had turned the way of the sun when leaving dock, and Barry had himself twice apologised for cursing the ship when she careened in the storm. Crossing the Atlantic, Bill remarked on a porpoise swimming north and said it was a sign of fine weather. When it veered due south he cursed it. Wacker refused to reach through the rungs of a ladder to retrieve a stray shackle. The Skipper had declined to sail as Mate on a ship whose name ended in the letter 'a' and touched cold steel if anyone named a furry relative of the hare.* He also resolutely refused to count the number of fish in the pound and always asked the Mate to calculate the catch from the Cod End. A solitary gull flying before the mast was 'known' to be following a corpse on the bed of the ocean,

* The author is likewise reluctant to record the name of this particular rodent.

and the Badger nodded when someone asked if his plain gold ear-ring was worn as a protection against drowning. Harry never cut his finger nails at sea for fear of provoking a storm and accepted without question his father's view that a sick trawlerman will not die until land is sighted. Buster met a clergyman when on his way to join *Arctic Fox* on a previous trip, and believing the encounter to be an ill omen, went back home and started out afresh by a different route. Having again encountered the same clergyman Buster went to the dock office and signed off. Nine of the crew carried a talisman of one sort or another, and the Skipper kept his first bairn's christening shoes tied to his bunk, and kept the child's christian name secret until after it was baptized. The galley boy was genuinely distressed when told it was unlucky to have thrown a bucket overboard (in his case it was, of course, accidental). The case of milk given to Mac the Bastard had first been deliberately damaged to honour the belief that to transfer it otherwise would bring bad luck to *Arctic Fox*. All Sorts demonstrated with some success that twigs from the shrub Rosemary grew well on board ship, but died ashore due to its name 'Ros Marinus', meaning 'dew of the sea'. He also kept a cobweb in a cornflake packet believing that it would stop bleeding if bound to a wound. The Chief took elaborate steps to avoid actually pointing out the star at the extreme tail of the Bear constellation, even though this would have given *Arctic Fox* her bearings at a critical moment. (It was visible long enough to be identified as Alkaid, to which no superstition is attached. The Chief merely considered it 'unlucky' to point at the moon or the stars). The raven – often found hunting in company with the bear – was, of course, white. Wacker believed that if it were photographed after having eaten the eyes of drowned sailors it would appear black. It would otherwise remain completely invisible through having failed to acquire the extra vision needed to effect its image on the camera film. The raven is credited with the power of curing blindness, and an oculist in Lincolnshire keeps a live raven in a cage. This bird is black, and the fact is recalled with more than passing interest by fishermen who have seen it.

The only superstition to affect them all was centred around the gull. Gulls are believed to embody the restless souls of dead mariners, especially the souls of men drowned at sea. Colin and Paddy went to endless trouble to save gulls from harm, and Paddy was the first to notice the solitary gull, mentioned above, flying a straight course atop *Arctic Fox's* bows. No one showed disbelief when Colin remarked on the mess-deck afterwards that the gull was keeping company with the body that once possessed it – to bring it rest as it drifted unseen along the ocean floor, unburied and alone in the dark water. This belief, apart from its emotional appeal to men themselves alone on the sea, was invested with a far stronger mystique than any other, and the moment the gull disappeared its absence was commented on by everyone except the Badger – a fact not without significance as his father's body was never recovered from the sea. Another fact of equal significance passed entirely without notice. The gull turned away from the ship at midnight on Friday the 13th of January, having flown before the mast for all of that day.

The two Deenies refused to be questioned on the subject of superstition – and, because of their place of work, were largely unobserved, except that one of them regularly infused Betony leaves in a teapot to relieve headaches. The only one noticeably free from superstition was the Whippit. Every one of the remainder was beset or bewitched in one way or another, but none would admit it of themselves – only of others. Apart from the Deenies and the Whippit, the Badger had no noticeable traits in this direction but, as mentioned earlier, he never missed a sailing for fear of drowning in the manner of his father. Once at sea, however, his continued survival was more a question of getting enough to eat – but he had promised never to remove his ear-ring and he never did.

Often more intuitive, but less fatalistic, the fishermen's wives are as superstitious as their men. Many women in Grimsby will not do the washing if their man sails on a Monday. Others will leave beds unmade for the same reason. A few will not say good-bye – and others never say good luck. Many refuse to watch a departing trawler out of sight, otherwise they believe they may never see it again. All, without exception, regard it as unlucky to call their man back once he has started out for his ship. If he looks back he invites danger when at sea. Rubber Nose's mother chased her son from Park Street to Humber Road, across the bridge and nearly to the docks, to hand over a pair of boot stockings – which she did after murmuring, 'Don't turn about, Son!'

Personal possessions left behind stay unmoved under a growing patina of dust until their owner returns. The Badger's mother kept a jackdaw which collected shiny objects and hid them in its cage. It avoided silver coins and a small steel mirror deliberately set down by the Badger, but pecked about in cupboards looking for objects he had carefully put away. This, according to his mother, was because she had 'told' the jackdaw of the reason why the mirror and money were not to be moved. She further 'told' it not to hang around outside the bookmakers because its late arrival home led to adverse changes in the weather. (She confirmed this by pointing to a fall in the barometer reading whenever this happened). If the bird croaked after sunset her son was safe, but if it sat on her left shoulder he was in danger. It was an ill omen if the jackdaw flew away from the sun, and this contrasts favourably with the Mate's view – namely, that it was a good omen when *Arctic Fox* turned the way of the sun before passing through the lock gates at Grimsby Port.

Some wives can repeat the source of many old superstitions, and confess to their belief in them. But it is when fact is scarce and legend increasingly hard to dispute that belief in superstition is strongest. And when legend and superstition have combined and become fortified with the belief of centuries they remain completely unassailable. Belief of this sort, however irrational, helps mariners to rationalise their fears and provides a thin life cord between them and the ever waiting ocean. They know the ocean will wait. With fate heavily on its side it will wait until the end of time if necessary.

Because so many of their beliefs are irrational trawlermen laugh at the superstitions connected with them. They grin at skippers who make wands out of wood and silver paper to encourage the sea to yield a rich harvest. They scorn mates who stick pins in potato men hoping to damn the good fortune of their rivals. They laugh at old hands who say it is wrong to whistle in case it brings the wind back. In the case of *Arctic Fox's* crew, all were tough men – as tough as they looked – apart from the gull they did not admit to being superstitious. To prove it they would shoot a new trawl on a Sunday and genuinely think nothing of it. Against all the omens, many wore green – almost with impunity. They smiled openly if anyone mentioned superstitions. But it was noticeable that their eyes didn't smile. And when alone on deck they often turned seaward, and it was possible to believe they were silently recanting to the one mistress none of them would ever possess.

No superstition attached to the ship, and no one had the least affection for her.

CHAPTER TWENTY-NINE

The Mate lost his footing on the deck and fell heavily. This, if he bothered to remember or if he remembered at all, was the tenth heavy fall he had taken in as many days. Others had fallen more often, but his job was the most arduous and certainly the most dangerous. A fall for him could mean death. Between feats of balancing he leaned far over the rail and made a sign, and then bawled an order. Every movement of men and ship was at his command. Even the Skipper became a human device for placing the ship exactly where the Mate wanted it. He barged across the deck. The Mate never walked – no one *walked* at hauling time. Men moved quickly with a practised economy of movement, and ran when they had to – but the Mate *barged* everywhere. It suited him. He was barging now, with his usual fiery contempt for obstacles – human or otherwise – and swearing, with a totally expected scorn, at nothing in particular. Hauling time was his finest moment. With the wind tearing at his face and the sea pouring over him he would shout for a bag becket, a short haul or a fathom of bolsh – and having used them, fling them away from him with enough force to maim the unwary.

In a man's world he stood alone. It would have been a betrayal of all theatrical values had the powerful searchlight followed anyone but him, and no 'star' had a more dedicated cast. Limbs tormented by the cruel weather, limbs now tired but with astonishing reflexes made involuntary movements of their own the moment he opened his mouth. With his carefully timed movements and ballerina footwork he made it all look so easy – and everyone knew it was one bastard of a job without room for a single mistake. There was no one to blame if £400 worth of fish escaped back into the sea. It was his fault if ten tons of trawling gear wrapped itself round the washer and bollards and took five hours to put right again. No one blamed the Skipper if a man got swept into the sea at hauling time. The coroner might, but not the crew. The crew blamed the Mate, and in his private moments the Mate accepted as inevitable the burden of his guilt. Responsibility made it so, and the responsibility remained his. He might have drunk himself out of commanding his own ship, but his authority on the deck was absolute.

No one but a fool would turn out on the deck drunk at hauling time – it just wasn't worth the risk. Alcohol freezing in the cavities of the brain destroys a man's balance even though he's convinced it doesn't. So it wasn't alcohol that made the Mate lose his footing and fall heavily to the deck. It was laughter. Just that. Laughter. By an extraordinary feat of gymnastics the Whippit had been hoisted high above the deck by the fore Gilson, and now swung upside down by his frock. Colin pulled him down and unhooked him before he swung out over the sea, and the crew raised a cheer. The extraordinary thing was he had managed to hold on to his chip sandwich which was covered with a thick layer of snow. He was to be given no chance to eat it, nevertheless.

Despite a noticeable abatement in the weather, the sea raged with undiminished fury and the manoeuvre required to keep the trawl clear of the screw was attempted many times before it was successful. For one thing, the distance from one wave top to

158

another was roughly equal to the length of the ship, and she was being carried upwards amidships before being thrown down with her bow and stern in the crests. The sea buried the decks a'midships when she fell, and men were flung from their stations and left washing about the foredeck, rolling over and over port to starboard, and then back again.

The Mate's ferocious temper matched the weather. In no time he was roaring above the wind.

'Pull in the slack on that headline. Don't just stand there –take that top wing inboard before it fouls on the door. Come on, some of you – JUMP TO IT!'

Four men rushed to the rail and worked the headline up the side, hand over hand.

'Get a move on – what are you? A lot of cripples? Heave on it! HEAVE! H-E-A-V-E!! Right. This time, then. All together H-E-A-V-E!!'

The trawl was being carried away from the ship under its own weight, aided by the force of the wind.

'H-E-A-V-E!'

Colin, Paddy, Wacker and Rubber Nose leaned out over the ship's side. The sea rose to meet them and the ship plunged violently downwards. Then she rose higher and higher until the sea was far below them. The great net tightened as the sea tried to drag it back into the ocean. The four men stood hard on their gains as the ship fell once more into the abyss. The Mate roared louder than ever.

'Get that bastard headline inboard. Pull on it – NOW!'

The last of the slack was gathered in just before the ship fell deep between the crests of the waves.

'Come on, COME ON! What's wrong with that after top wing?'

Colin said the Grummet had parted.

'Don't just stand there, then. Use the gilson.' The Mate cupped his hands. 'THE GILSON! . . . useless bastard.'

The four hands rushed to the after gallows just as the sea rose to eye level and drenched everyone within reach.

'It doesn't need four of you to do THAT – who's on this bastard winch – a fucking mermaid?'

Three hands rushed back to the winch.

'Heave on the Yo-Yo! HEAVE on it, then! Has everyone gone home or something?'

And then a number of orders all given at once.

'Fanny. Heave on the *Fanny*. Bag Becket. Double twine. A strand – quick, a STRAND. Short haul. Surge on the fore gilson. SURGE on in, then.'

From first to last all these commands had been given – and all of them obeyed – in just under two minutes. The Mate repeated this 'performance' day and night, every three hours, for ten days – unless he was watch below. And he never lost the tremendous power of his voice. There were many who wished he would.

The Badger led the cheers and it was his cheer that had the strongest ring of irony. The anger of the last few days melted away. *Arctic Fox's* tired, dirty, unshaven crew had been immunised with nature's sweetest anodyne – success. The Skipper had *at last* found a 'fish shop'. Coming inboard was four tons of fish. With the Cod End released they thundered on to the foredeck, and soon all the pounds were filled with the rich, bountiful harvest of the sea.

There were cod fish, large and firm to the touch. Some were ten years old and weighed 180 pounds, most were 20 or 30 pounds, and all were in good condition. Livers were large and accounted for about 8 per cent of the total weight of each fish. Some of the cod carried food on their gills and were on passage to other regions having already travelled many hundreds of miles. A few of these had been tagged at Reykjavik (Iceland) to assist in the study of migration, growth and other matters. Each tag carries a reward of 5s. Harry was the only one known to return them and claim the money.

Cat fish abound in this part of the world and numbers of them now lay in the pounds. The 'cats' had soft, yellow skins free from scales and marked with black spots. Their muscular bodies flexed and writhed, and resembled those of a powerful reptile. Their mouths were large, and filled with long, sharp teeth which, if

160

they closed over a boot or a man's hand, could not be torn away until the head was crushed. 'Cats' (Anarhichas Minor) take longer to die than most fish when taken from the sea (with the probable exception of monk fish), and are always handled with caution by the deckhands who keep their fingers away from their snapping jaws.

Buster stood in the pound with both his feet in a liver basket – and wouldn't gut any 'Cats' unless he had to! The Badger eyed him with contempt and then remarked . . .

'It's not yer feet you have to bother about, Buster, it's yer hands. Deckie I know lost a finger. Cat bit it off.'

So what?' replied Colin. 'Still had three others, didn't he?'

'Yes, but this was his courting finger – fancy losing yer *courting* finger.'

A number of heads nodded in sympathy.

Among the catch was a salmon. At the end of the spawning season the Arctic salmon separate and make their way singly down the Spitsbergen Fjords, the contours of which continue under the sea with their structure and depth remaining unaltered, for a considerable distance. As the Arctic salmon is able to withstand changes in temperature and increased salinity it survives the change. Salmon are rarely caught in Polar regions and are therefore much valued, particularly for their flavour. This one had already been smuggled aft and would not be seen again until it appeared on the mess-deck table.

Also included in the haul was a giant 27-stone halibut, which needed a fathom of bolsh lashed securely round its tail and the forward gilson to lift it down beside the washer. It needed careful handling, too. A halibut of this size could have crushed a man's hand between its armoured gill covers, and on this giant they were still opening and closing like the jaws of a vice.

Once more *Arctic Fox* put her gear down and in three hours she had made another record haul. Her total for the twenty-four hours stood at 25 tons and most of it was 'shelfing quality'. Amongst the catch was a 36½ lb. haddock measuring 45 in. long – possibly a world record for this type of fish! On her next haul she repeated her success but the trawl was severely damaged by a Narwhal. This great sea animal had earlier been trapped in the ice by a sudden freezing of one of the leads in the sea. Its habit is to keep to open water when it can find it in order to surface for air. Mostly it lives 12 miles off shore in the deep ocean along the border of the firm unbroken ice, but the severe conditions in the area had made it a prisoner, and *Arctic Fox* caught it in her trawl. Normally, the Narwhal is coloured black along its back with spotted flanks and a white belly. This one was entirely white and measured 15ft. 0 in. long. Extending from its head was a 9 ft. 0 in. long spiralled ivory tusk similar to the one supposed to have originated with the fabled Unicorn. It is known to trawlermen as the 'Sea Unicorn' and regarded as a delicacy by Eskimoes, who dry its meat for winter food – guests bring their own blubber along to eat with it. The Sea Unicorn is himself a fussy eater and will eat shrimps only when there's a shortage of Greenland halibut. The all-white Sea Unicorn is rare, even in Arctic waters, and has itself given rise to certain legends. In Elizabethan times the powdered ivory from its spear was considered a suitable formula against unwelcome forms of magic, and as late as 1789 drinking cups made from 'Unicorn's' horn symbolized the belief in the efficacy of the horn against poison. Today, this harmless animal is cut to ribbons to provide most of the world with ski lashes. It is just possible that the Norsemen from Iceland traded the horn of the Unicorn as genuine 'Horse Unicorn'. There is a very fine example in the Abbey of St Denis which, judging by the photograph, is cerainly the tusk from a fully-grown Narwhal. This one was not likely to find anyone bidding for him at the Grimsby fish market, and he was hoisted back into the sea where he rolled over in gratitude before diving deep into the ocean. Meanwhile, *Arctic Fox* mended her trawl and carried on fishing.

Hands blue to the wrists knitted diamond mesh to diamond mesh and repaired both top wings with a speed and precision that might have impressed the Royal School of Needlework.

CHAPTER THIRTY

Two men, so unalike, now less accustomed to holding back their differences, stood together on the bridge. The distance between them widened and narrowed as the ship breasted the sea, tilted the bridge in a steep climb, then canted in a sudden angular dive. The Skipper leaned forward from his customary position and hunched his shoulders as though turning away a rebuke. Narrowing his eyes, he took in with a glance a dozen aspects of the ship's appearance and without turning round he spoke.

'Yes?'

His face, seen in profile, lit by the suffused glow from the Radar set, was a study in the loneliness of command. The Mate had given very little thought to what he was about to say, but he was pleased with the opportunity it now gave him. Praise was due, and thanks, too. He was there to offer both.

Over pots of tea. In the interval between endless games of poker. In between turning the pages of last month's newspapers and the silence of familiar, infinitely wearisome chat, a satisfaction infused with gratitude carried upward on ripples of feeling towards the bridge . . . The old man had got a trip in – done better than they expected. They'd worked for their success – suffered for it, too, but the Skipper had pulled it off and someone should give him a grudging 'thank you'.

The Mate began . . .

'Well, er, the lads are pleased – I thought you'd like to know.'

He was about to make the remark more personal, but after glancing at the hunched back, changed his mind. By way of reply the Skipper leaned a little longer than usual against the starboard lookout window before turning to ask: 'How many of them will you be telling to sign off?'

The tone was dry and curt, as always, but the question was clearly unexpected.

'Sackings, you mean?'

'That's what one usually means by signing off.'

'Well . . . three. But do we have to . . . ?'

The Skipper cut in abruptly.

'Does that include the two deckmen who threatened to sign off earlier on?'

'No, only one of that pair. But can't we forget . . . ?'

Once more the Skipper stopped the Mate short.

'What's special about the other one?'

The reply, in which coolness and a lack of esteem were blended, was meant to kill the conversation dead – and it did just that.

'You ungrateful bastard.'

The Skipper, his face grey like the ocean at dawn, turned slowly towards the chart room.

The Mate barged his way aft and entered the crowded mess-deck. Characteristically, his broad muscular shoulders were drawn back and his chin thrust out. Ten men and one boy made way for him as he pushed his way between them. Pulling down the tops of his thigh boots he flung himself back against the corner bulk-head seat and accepted a cigarette which three eager hands sought to light. They gave him a moment or two and then all spoke at once.

'What did the Skip say?'

'Was he pleased?'

'Are we getting a gash dram?'

Blood covered the backs of the Mate's hands, which were scarred with ice burns and covered with salt-water boils – mostly at the wrists. For some moments his hands claimed all of his attention. Delay wouldn't help – they had to be told something.

'Sorry, kiddos, we chose the wrong moment.'

'How d'you mean?'

'Just that. He wasn't in the mood.'

The Mate looked up and met each of the eleven faces in turn.

'Later, perhaps. Barry . . . he talks to Barry.'

The questioning should have stopped there. He wanted it to stop. Then Harry spoke.

'Didn't he want to listen?'

In a quiet voice the Mate replied : 'It wouldn't help to repeat it all again, not now.'

Around him the slow change from expectation to surprise plunged into a moment of noisy protest and finally to a nameless dislike. Who did that bastard on the bridge think he was? Abruptly, the Mate stood up. It was Barry he wanted to see. In the gangway outside the mess-deck the Mate hesitated before turning quickly towards Barry's berth. The lumbering gait – it never failed to confirm an enviable sense of balance – made no sound above the roar of the engine. The short, powerful body swayed easily with the movement of the ship, and the firm steps pointed to a man treading familiar ground. Only the set of his shoulders was disturbing.

The Mate opened the door marked 'BOSUN' without bothering to knock. It was the sort of thing expected of him, and Barry showed no surprise as he closed his book and reached out for his tobacco tin. They talked for an hour. For most of it Barry just listened – the cruel impediment in his speech made conversation a bitter struggle. In the long pauses between words a rapport slowly established itself. From this rapport one man gained friendship, the other found understanding. They had been talking, not about themselves, but about the Skipper. The man whose utter – often ruthless – dedication Barry had lately admired and understood. It was an odd sort of quality to find Barry admiring, until one remembered how great his own ambitions had once been. The Mate had failed to see it for what it was because his uncomplicated mind hadn't understood the compulsion behind it. Now that he had, it was only one short step to realising that this was the one thing he had never found in himself. As a mariner he was the better man of the two. He had a natural authority and an instinctive feeling for command. In trawling, these were not enough. Barry had said so, and regrettably he was right.

Once inside the chart room, the Skipper lifted the lid of the box bearing the date 1804 and glanced at the familiar surname before clipping fresh charts to the table. With quick, confident fingers he began charting a course. Having plotted the course line and laid it off on the charts the Skipper calculated the bearing, which he recorded as a compass notation, and having carefully checked all the figures, pulled the charts from the table and pushed them back inside one of the numbered drawers. Privately he had decided to cant the ship and start the long journey back to England.

Above the mast an elegant tern flew with the ship. Suddenly it turned in a swift dive to grab a sand eel left on the rail. The shadow of a large bird with pointed wings fell across the fish pounds – a white falcon ready to catch the tern in flight. This great bird climbed upwards before turning into a dive, and in a moment the tern was gripped in strong talons and carried across the sea.

'We always see a falcon on the last day of fishing,' someone remarked.

This was not true, but trawlermen are always on the look-out for some sign that fishing is coming to an end, and any excuse is used in the hope of finding out.

The eightieth haul provided *Arctic Fox* with a further four ton of fish. All hands turned out to gut it.

The long swell rolled across the sea. The clouds parted and the starlit ocean was empty to the four horizons. For one significant moment the ship rolled at ease and then turned through 180 degrees before heading due south. Her furrowed wake left a question-mark on the ocean.

As she gathered way the Tannoy burst into life with a rush of atmospherics.

'Bring the doors in. Cod End inboard. Get those fish down soon as you can and then lash the trawl alongside.'

And then in a burst of rare humour the Skipper added: 'We're going home – if anyone's interested – send one of the watch up to the bridge.'

And that was all. 'Home' was a mere 140 hours away to the south.

CHAPTER THIRTY-ONE

Arctic Fox started her greyhound dash back across the Northern Seas at her best speed of 12½ knots. She showed considerable 'sea-kindliness', but rolled heavily due to the weight of fish she was now carrying. Pitching was confined to a rhythmic curtsey before her scarred and twisted forepeak lifted over the crests with ease. *Arctic Fox's* brazen manner proclaimed her view that the low Arctic had punished her enough and was finally content to let her go. The air temperature, however, was still low enough to freeze the inside of the lungs, and the distribution of ice on the decks made the helm difficult to handle.

On the ship all external features still appeared many times larger than they were. The belaying cleats either side of the forepeak, although mounted only a foot above deck level, were buried under four feet of ice which deflected the sharp blade of an axe as though itself made of steel. The ship viewed from the whaleback looking towards the stern had every appearance of a floating iceberg.

January is the month of total darkness. December is certainly the deepest. But in these latitudes the clouds hide the moon and stars, and the snowfall now raging obliterated the few remaining icebergs from the Radar screen. On the bridge the windows were lowered to aid sighting, but were soon closed again. There had been more than one recorded instance of men being struck by sea-spray which has entered the eyes and frozen the cornea.

There were hazards still, but the danger of capsize had gone for good and with the steady approach of warmer latitudes the ice would begin to melt back into the sea and the heavy list correct itself. Soon *Arctic Fox* would no longer be hidden by the dark, and it was noticeable that during the day the crew began watching the sky both at the summit and down on the horizon. Hour by hour it was possible to notice how the sea currents kept the water open, and the explosion of icebergs became almost monotonous. The dry air gave way to humidity at the rate of one degree every six hours, and the solitary ptarmigan trailing the after mast finally turned back towards the Pole. So many small changes discernible to the experienced eye, so many subtleties of behaviour, meant that the emptiness, the enduring cold and endless night were soon to be no more.

Some of this feeling of release had communicated itself to the crew and left them restless. The low Arctic cannot fail to make an impression, and those who have witnessed its beauty and touched, however fleetingly, its cruel, desolate places often long to go back. Its aura has enticed hundreds of men who have died there, and others – either for adventure or gain – will die there too.

Once physical contact with the Arctic has been broken – by the closing of a bulkhead door or the sliding of a hatch cover – the pulsebeat of the engine can be heard giving counterpoint to the very heart of the ocean, and the bridge log acts as a metronome. The mind has been tuned, the senses sharpened, so that accustomed movement becomes charged with drama. For the least tangible of reasons the fingers of the mind reach out to touch the ice and to feel it anaesthetize the face until the cruel burns no longer bring pain but fragments of a sublime and transfiguring experience. These moments, however irrational, are for some men moments of reality. The Arctic, because of its proximity, is real, and the rest of the world remote. Although vulnerable and alone, men feel an indefinable harmony and sense of eternity with it. The pulse beat of the engine is the beat of nature's heart, and for a moment her simple secret is the secret of human life. Something has altered their destiny, and they are leaving that something behind.

Few trawlermen acknowledge any predilection for the inhuman wastes of the Arctic regions and tend instead to rationalise their strange longing. They call it simply 'sea-madness' or 'sea fever' or in a few instances 'the death wish'. Doubtless someone in the cloistered calm of Harley Street has already found an explanation buried deep in the cathartic principle overlaid with the theory of panlogism, but no one could ever match the Badger's theory – unprintable – in the mind of anyone fortunate enough to hear it.

Predictably – because she was a woman – *Arctic Fox* decided she was not tired after all. The Arctic had nearly claimed her, but at the last minute it had relented. Furthermore she was going home. Time to celebrate. At the slightest touch of a steam valve she sent her glistening bow clawing the sky before gliding into the hollows. As the revolutions mounted she rolled like a seal at play, and twice succeeded in ringing her own bell. (This caprice was frowned on, and the hammer was lashed secure.) Music blared from her loud speakers as she thrust her scarred body across the last few miles of the Arctic Ocean. Eagerly she leapt ahead, holding a dead straight course like she'd never done before.

'Can't think what's come over her, she's doing 13 knots already,' said a beaming Chief Engineer.

Freed from the burden of her trawl she headed direct for the wide Atlantic, refusing to be held. Determined to get home. Grateful for the chance. The ocean lay flat to the horizon. It threw spindrift over her bows like a gentle Benediction, and the wind dried tear-drops from her rails in implicit homage.

CHAPTER THIRTY-TWO

The term 'Arctic Circle' is an abstraction. An astronomical concept denoting the line 66 degrees, 33 minutes 03 seconds along the parallel of north latitude. Considered by the knowledgeable to represent the limits of floating ice and to encompass a region where the mean temperature in the warmest month does not reach 50 degrees Fahrenheit, this arbitrary division remains unacclaimed by trawlermen but is seemingly observed by the Arctic gull.

Within a day of *Arctic Fox* passing across the 66th latitude the Mollies turned and left the ship. Confined by some strange chemistry to within the Arctic Circle they stayed just long enough to give a display of showy extravagance. As if they were aware of the beauty of their natural form they rehearsed arabesques, often in pairs, before turning back across the ocean in one long stream. Following each other they flew north on a spiced wind to an alien shore, there to skirt the black rocks cut with the austere incision of jet before returning in quest of another harvester of the sea.

Arctic Fox had served them well. Nearly a hundred had been picked up off the deck, and a few had been freed from between the warp wires aft of the towing block. Those that fell to the deck would have been doomed without assistance. Mollies are unable to rise from a flat plain, and within a short time their feet freeze solid – leaving them incapable of moving or changing their position.

One of the last to leave made sad music with his wings and shed faintly discernible particles of down by way of remembrance. Their leaving marked not so much the end of fishing, but a prelude to the coming symphony of colour and an end to the everlasting fight against the cold. The crew watched the last of them go with something less than their customary detachment and even the Skipper paid them an off-hand compliment. Usually his voice reflected what he thought, but for once it expressed true feeling.

'It would be lonely out here without those hungry little bastards following us about.'

Almost the last bird to go, and easily the ship's most loyal follower, was a majestic Caspian tern. He flew always in the light from the ship, and if one of the searchlights came on, moved quickly over and continued his journey flying along its beam – gliding motionless against the wind. If left too long without attention he shouted insults at anyone who appeared, and showed his pique by refusing to dive for the fish thrown in his path.

He refused to be ignored, and his plumage alone made it difficult to do so. On his head he wore a large black cap extending to below the eye. A bright coral-red bill set off the white feathers and gave contrast to the short black legs and small, equally black feet, whilst a faint touch of mascara around the eyes underlined his fondness for showing off.

He would dive on a tin thrown into the sea and tear the label off it before it sank. Having completed a number of aerial manoeuvres which included gliding, darting, hovering and tumbling over, he plunged under the sea before rushing back to receive his applause, which he accepted with what sounded like a low chuckle.

This bold, elegant bird stayed one day longer than the gulls and before turning away called incessantly for an hour or more. The cry blended in a strange wild harmony, infinitely variable in tone, with the restless sea which held the tern its captive. The echo of that cry could still be heard after the tern had gone, and Colin went out on deck to make sure it was not trapped some-where. He didn't find the bird, but was sure he could still hear its plaintive cry.

CHAPTER THIRTY-THREE

The last days of the voyage. Frocks, seaboots and sou'westers have given way to jeans, clumpers, smocks and verminous jerseys. The washer had been dismantled, the decks scrubbed with deck brushes. Twine, old net and stranded warp dumped over the side. In the forehold, Wacker and Colin were making up a complete new trawl. The Bosun knelt on the foredeck unpicking the Cod Ends from the belly and baitings and making them ready for the next trip. Below decks, in the fishroom, boards and battens were being scrubbed, the rose bowl flushed and cleaned, the staging taken down and stowed away in the empty pounds for'ard. With the below-decks work finished to the Mate's satisfaction, the hatches were banged up and secured. With the hatches closed the fishroom temperature fell to 32 degrees. On the mess-deck the galley boy scrubbed the fiddle batons which divided up the tables and washed the wooden bulkhead panels with vinegar and warm water. The cook scoured the galley and blackleaded the stove. Overhead pipes were repainted silver and the pantry emptied and scrubbed. The engine room looked immaculate, the brasswork and steel rails along the cat-walks gleamed brightly. All supporting stanchions were newly painted, and ferrules and bosses burnished with wire wool. Bunks were being scrubbed out, mats scrubbed with sea water and hung out on the boat-deck to dry in the wind. Berth doors were treated with furniture polish and companion-ways scrubbed and left to dry. On the bridge, the Skipper's carpet was taken out and carefully brushed, and his surprisingly well-appointed bathroom would not have disgraced a house-proud wife ashore in its state of cleanliness.

The bridge itself was partly the Badger's responsibility, but he was always hard to find at this time and difficult to handle when he was found. The Badger was not overfond of such pastimes as cleaning brass and scrubbing floors and could only be ambushed into these irrelevancies by stealth. Someone would whisper there was a gash dram of rum on the bridge if he went right away. The Badger would lumber off at great speed, stepping over buckets and polish, and in an amiable manner of one seeking information ask what all the activity was in aid of. Once on the bridge, the watch locked the door behind him and kept him prisoner until he had made enough mess to be let out again. Afterwards, the Badger hired the Whippit as look-out, appearing in public only after the work was finished. This game went on trip after trip, and was likely to succeed for as long as the Badger's thirst was greater than his caution.

The watch's current efforts to capture the Badger ended in the usual 'Cops and Robbers' chase throughout the ship, but they finally cornered him in the galley and dragged him along to the bridge where they locked him in. He plugged in the Skipper's electric razor and shaved himself in the compass reflector binnacle before banging to be let out. As usual, he had done no cleaning. In his rush to get down the bridge companion way to safety he collided with the Bosun on his way up to inspect the cleaning of the bridge.

'I've left a bit of cleaning for you, Barry. I know you like a bit of brass to rub while you're on watch.'

Considering that Barry's status absolved him from 'a bit of cleaning' his reply was quite gentle.

'Good fer nowt son o' therein is Badger.'

'We've *all* got to do our bit,' was the obscure reply.

'Yew was kean enif o' thar job fo'st off wen yew smelt thar rum.'

'I don't work for bribes.' The Badger's attempt at hauteur wasn't very successful.

'Yew doant werk at all 'ness thar can 'elp et.'

With that Barry climbed to the bridge to gaze at the bright green brasswork which confronted him and perhaps wonder at the mirror-clean patch in the reflector binnacle where the Badger had just shaved himself.

From the boat-deck looking aft, the wake opened out like a lace fan as the miles dropped astern. In a few hours the sun would rise out of the sea and as *Arctic Fox* closed with the land (eighty miles away) old hands would be sure they could smell the soil and the rich pasture along the rocky headland. Countless gulls took up escort duty and a school of porpoise ran like torpedoes along the bow. Pointing the way home, southward. Ahead on the port bow, other ships were beating across the wide Atlantic on the long voyage back to England. Ships from Grimsby, Hull, Aberdeen and Lowestoft – quickly identified by the knowledgeable Bosun as they raced to catch their respective markets. Ships returning from Cape Farewell with ice melting on their ratlines and fore-peak. Ships returning from the North Cape of Iceland with their deck lights still burning. Modern diesels with raked bows edged forward in the race as their engines opened up to counter the effects of the freshening head wind and cross swell. Steam trawlers with high stacks plunged gallantly on with men still gutting fish on their foredecks and conical baskets still showing – denoting they had stopped at the last minute to make another haul and get a trip in.

Leading this frantic race was Mac the Bastard, quickly identified by his canary-coloured trawler. His bow and foredeck completely submerged by the sea, he was once again out in front and gave every appearance of staying there. As the wind veered round he disappeared completely within his own smokescreen and emerged each time further ahead of his rivals. With his boilers under full pressure his maximum speed was reckoned at 10 knots, yet he had just overhauled a 13-knot diesel steaming full ahead and was fast disappearing over the skyline. As would have been noticed, Mac had that truly British gift of backing into the limelight. He had no personal longing to be liked and was the least interested of anyone as to what others thought of him. Yet everything he did ended in extremes of involvement for others. No matter how improbable the story, disbelief surrendered to credence the instant it was known Mac was involved, and in no time people had taken sides. Some defended whatever it was he had done, whilst others denounced him. Soon, they changed sides – and as often as not united against him. He didn't help matters by being aggressively tactless, but even so desirable a quality as 'giving a helping hand' was thought of as treachery.

So it was on this occasion as reports started to come in over the radio telephone of Mac's latest escapade. It appeared that Mac had been on the air setting out strategic truths concerning the location of fish which resulted in a young potential rival turning round and steaming forcefully towards the Pole, whilst Mac went the other way. The rival caught nothing, and lost his complete trawl – whilst Mac caught more fish than he could handle. After beating relentlessly around the Arctic for hours on end the young skipper found Mac's trawler laid so as to give the deckmen time to clear the catch before shooting away. Mac was leaning out of the bridge window dropping bottles into the sea. The visitor came alongside until both trawlers lay close enough for the outward surge of their bow waves to break against each other before racing into the outer darkness. Moments later both ships were riding less than a fathom apart and Mac thought he was about to be boarded. He ordered all hands to appear on deck and a number of death-dealing devices appeared from beneath tarpaulins. Heaving lines snaked across from the visitor and were promptly axed by Mac's crew.

'Fuck off afore I ram yer,' shouted Mac, adding as an afterthought, 'yer skinny streak o' piss.'

The reply was no less conciliatory and ended with the well-bred assumption that Mac was a drunken old bastard whose views on where to find fish were wildly visionary.

'Get knotted.'

Mac would be made to pay for the lost trawl.

'Double knotted.'

And reported for trespassing.

'Piss off.'

His Gaffers would get a full report.

'Bollocks.'

And the Board of Trade . . .

'Bollocks to them too.'

Threats of this kind were obviously of no use so the visitor threw fenders over his port rail and drifted on helm and engines until both vessels touched. Mac's only reaction was to screw the cap back on to one of his bottles and leave the bridge. He returned moments later carrying a far-from-ineffective rifle. In fact, as it appeared above the still of the bridge it was seen to have telescopic sights and an impressively long barrel. By way of ultimatum Mac rammed a cartridge into the breach, raised the sights level with his eye and took first pressure on the trigger. His opponent stepped back inside the bridge. Mac corrected the range and followed him. His target again moved, this time to the floor. The rifle steadied until it was in line with the young skipper's skull. Mac started to count . . . five, four, three, two . . . Slowly, imperceptibly at first, the two ships began to drift apart. The pulse-beat of the visitor's engines grew louder as the distance widened, and soon they were riding the swell more than two cables apart. Mac, it was agreed, would certainly have fired – and done so intending to kill. His tongue, however, could be equally deadly. Claiming the last word he leaned out of the bridge and made his departing visitor the beneficiary of some advice which, for known reasons, was physically impossible.

This 'incident' was not without historical interest. The young Skipper had lost his gear, including both doors, on bearing 72 degrees 16 North, 28 degrees 41 East. This was the last navigational position of the Scharnhorst, and it is likely that her wreckage was responsible for the loss. Mac was not to blame, as the wreck is marked on the charts and the young Skipper should have noticed this.

We leave Mac the Bastard at this point, as his course took him away to his home port of Aberdeen – through the Pentland Firth, round Duncansby Head and past Wick, before closing with the land off Peterhead. His home port was expecting him, that much was clear from the radio telephone, but there was a subdued quality to the voice that informed him he would be first home. There was, however, nothing subdued about the lusty reply or the belch which accompanied it.

The last glimpse of Mac the Bastard showed him completely in character. With the help of binoculars he was seen closing the rear of a convoy of trawlers. Great clouds of smoke poured from his funnel and as he opened up still more his bow wave blotted him and them from view. He emerged from behind a wall of spray and after some free-style manoeuvring rocketed down *the centre* of the convoy and vanished. According to one observer Mac's speed was $15\frac{1}{2}$ knots. Messrs. J. Lewis and Sons Limited would doubtless be impressed.

From the wheel position Paddy enquired, 'How does he do it?' 'It's rumoured,' said Rubber Nose, answering from the wing, 'that Mac has eight people sitting on the safety valve in three-hour watches . . . I've 'eard he chains 'em down.'

Over the radio, skippers exchanged banter and avoided asking questions to which they would not get answers – size of catch, state of market, landing days. All the time watching speed indicators and rev counters, mentally urging their ships on for a market tide and a low berth number.

On board *Arctic Fox* the radio was silent. The Skipper switched it off and returned to his cabin. His father had stood where he now stood. Facing the same glasses chattering in the rack beside the barometer. The same chintz seat covers and un-nautical red carpet. Although it served as the Skipper's home for forty-four weeks of the year it was as impersonal as the pubs off Riby Square. A refuge, and nothing else. He felt no sentiment for it or his ship, and it was noticeably empty of anything belonging

176

to him. The engraved metal ashtray, (from which a superstitious hand had scored out the words 'Good Luck') had belonged to a previous occupant. The books in the rack had been left behind by someone else. The medical dictionary and reference tables belonged to the ship. The current *Reed's Nautical Almanac* remained unopened in its birthday wrapping, with the greetings card still inside and visible through the paper. The 'Gonks' and talismen swinging from the deckhead no longer had an owner and the marine calendar was out of date. Only his wife's photograph gave him an identity outside of himself, and that stayed mostly in the canvas grip already packed beside the wardrobe cupboard, which significantly contained all the deck gear he used as a mate and nothing of the trawler skipper's traditional bridge rig ('Fearnaught' trousers, a coarse speckled jersey, canvas shoes and a variety of check caps).

The Skipper picked up the ship's Manifest which had been signed by the crew and added his signature without glancing at any of its details. For some moments he sat staring into space before placing the ship's articles in the container provided for their transfer ashore. He lifted from the table the Certificate of Registry endorsed with the ship's Signal Letters and bearing his name as her lawful Captain. It was possible to believe that he'd not bothered to read this document more than once, or looked with understandable pleasure at his own name printed on it. Normally it was locked away, only to be taken from the ship on a change in her command. The Skipper never locked it away, and often it fell to the floor where it lay unclaimed until someone picked it up. The Skipper held the Registry as though carefully weighing its contents in one hand, and then replaced it on the cabin table.

When the Mate knocked and entered with *Arctic Fox's* impressive tally of fish, his Captain's only response was to ask if it was correct. When the Mate replied that it was he was told to 'leave it there – I'll look at it later'. The tally recorded the best trip the ship had made in all her sea-going career, yet the man most responsible for it was seemingly disinterested – or reluctant to pick it up and read it. The alert, tired face which in the dim light looked like an unbearded Christ was not the face of a mariner, and some felt it would not take much to make him give up the sea for good. But the sea was in his blood, so the choice would never be his alone. Bill referred to him privately as an 'anti hero', without perhaps taking into account the Skipper's iron will and cool determination to succeed. Both were very considerable, and dispelled the doubts which the expression in his eyes often gave rise to. To the few who were able to watch him at work during long hours without sleep, against savage conditions to which his own singular lack of maritime experience added at least one moment of extreme peril, he remained a strange man. Although catching fish was his only consideration, and all his energy and nerve were given to this end, he left a feeling – however ill-defined – that he hoped somehow not to succeed. The man best able to assist him was consulted on the broader issues such as changing trawls or steaming to a new fishing location, but was left in ignorance of vital matters which might have provided a pointer to the thinking behind them. Some of the deliberate risks taken in order to find and catch fish were wrapped around with a remoteness and insularity which the Skipper's authority did much to maintain, and the impression it left was one of deliberate concealment. At least one of the decisions reached in this context was not cerebral but emotional – arising from frustration and the spectre of failure, and resulting in *Arctic Fox* penetrating to within twenty-six miles of the southern tip of Spitsbergen and making a record haul. It so happened that it succeeded brilliantly, but was not as 'objective' as appeared at the time.

Possibly catharis had some place in his make-up and was given the full effect of its meaning by other inconsistencies which trawling made it impossible to limit or control. To his crew he remained something of an enigma, and might have appeared so to himself. We shall never know. His wife worshipped him this side of idolatry, but his response to her tearful embrace at each arrival and departure was as taciturn as the onlooker had every right to expect. His assembled children he patted with distant affection before walking slowly to the waiting taxi. He might turn to glance back at the sea, but never spared a glance for the ship, its crew or anyone waiting in the hope of a word with him.

If the Skipper was silent and uncertain the crew was not. All the showers were in use, and men sang lustily as three weeks' growth of beard was shaved off. The only worried man was the conscientious All Sorts who was trying to cook a meal for twenty-one men on a stove fired with wooden boxes and bits of cardboard. The coal had been lost when *Arctic Fox* collided with a growler.

Crossing the foredeck the Badger took off his sou'wester and his hair caught on the wind like a candle flame. From the bridge look-out Paddy asked: 'Aya gettin' on, Badger?'

The reply was breathless.

'I've 'eard a rumour.'

On the quarterdeck the Badger thrust his sou'wester at the galley boy and tore past. Outside the drying room the Badger kicked off his thigh boots and grabbed the Whippit by the arm.

'I've just 'eard a rumour.'

Together they lumbered along the gangway. Buster bobbed out from somewhere.

'Something on?'

'It's rumour time.'

'How much?'

Still running, the Badger shouted over his shoulder: 'Likely be two bottles apiece if we hurry on.'

Fighting for the lead, these three pushed and elbowed their way up the bridge companionway and stood breathless outside the Captain's cabin.

'Port or sherry?' the Sparks asked the Badger.

'*Both*,' answered the Badger.

'*Both*,' echoed the Whippit.

'Port or sherry?' the Sparks asked Buster.

'One of each will do – for a start.'

'I'm afraid, Buster, that's all there *will* be.'

'And I'll take your bottle of brandy instead of the money you lost at poker.'

'I really don't see why . . .'

The Badger turned, and one freckled fist grabbed the Sparks' left nipple.

'Now then, darlin', must pay yer gamblin' debts.'

He let the nipple go.

'And while we're at it I'll 'ave that half case of beer you promised me way back.'

'Next trip, Badger. I haven't got it now.'

The Badger pulled the Sparks towards him until their noses touched.

'You an' I know, don't we, that there isn't any next trip – you're signing off, duckie. I saw it in yer face a fortnight back.'

Stroking his ginger hair back over his ears, the Badger said confidentially: 'Bring it with yer. I'll be on the mess-deck.'

On the mess-deck the party gathered way slowly. Colin, Wacker and Paddy drifted in carrying a bottle each, by which time the Badger, Whippit and Buster had 'found' a bottle of rum apiece.

'Looks like you three are all right,' remarked Colin, trying to find a place to sit down.

'Does an' all,' replied the Badger with a chuckle. 'Can we do owt for you, like?'

'You can take yer titfer 'n' scarper.'

'Don't be like that – what about a bit of a yarn, Buster?'

Buster related the story of the girl who caught her tits in the mangle which they knew by heart. Outside, in the gangway, the Sparks' falsetto voice could be heard.

'Thank you, lads. Make way if you please.'

The Badger stood up. In tones of utterly chilling grandeur he announced: 'HIS ROYAL HIGHNESS!' And then he blew a raspberry in the Sparks' ear.

'Filthy beast.'

'Have you got yer frillies on ready for going ashore?'

'Some rotten bastard's starched his knickers.'

'Lads,' pleaded the Sparks, 'I'm rather tired, if you don't mind.'

'Yes,' mused the Whippit, 'You must be fair clapped out – sharpening all them pencils.'

'You are all *most* unreasonable.'

180

'How long is it since you had one of those wild slow motion dreams you used to tell us about?'

Harry arrived.

'What's going on 'ere, then?'

'The Sparks' showing us 'is bum.'

'Give 'im a can o' beer an' 'e'll let you whip 'im with a tooth brush.'

'They tell me,' Paddy addressed the Sparks, 'that you're a bit of an arse bandit. I've got a fair old chopper here anytime yer feeling fruity.'

Bill arrived carrying a two-tier wedding cake.

'What's this then?' enquired Buster. 'You 'aven't got you'sen spliced?'

'Aye, well, I nearly did.'

'How come? Put a bun in the oven?'

'I met this lass, that's all. Peggy, her name was.'

(Chorus) 'Tell us about it then.'

'We met outside t' Gaiety. Hair in a rollers under a scarf . . . pretty lass though . . .' Bill accepted a jam jar full of sherry. 'That's how she was. She said, "You on the docks?" I said, "No, trawlers. Bloody two day millionaire." I went for Sunday tea – Thorold Street. You could smell the unemployment – her Mum taking back the egg she'd borrowed and coming back with a twist of tea held behind her back. We did our courtin' at t'end of the sixfoot after dark. Leastways we started at sixfoot and then moved upstairs. She liked it well enough. I told her I didn't reckon on getting wed yetawhile. She said, "Oh" like she was surprised. "Why not?" I said, "It's early on yet". And then she told me of the cake and how she booked the 'all for reception. She didn't mention t'furniture she bought till later. Nearly bloody trapped I was. I said, 'old on a bit, lass, I 'aven't proposed to ye yet" and I thought of addin' I was'en going to neither. She said, "Ye don't have to do owt like proposin'. Don't talk bloody wet". I said, "Aye, I can see that right enough. Ye've arranged t'honeymoon as well I suppose?". She said, "Aye, o'course I 'ave – Cleethorpes! Grow up a bit will yer." I said, "Thanks for tellin' me, anyroad". She said. "Why, summut wrong?" I said, "You can unbook bloody 'all for a start''. She said, "Ye cheeky bloody monkey''. After that I grabbed me bike and pissed off as fast as me legs would go. She called out, "Are you with me then?" I shouted back, "I am now, luv, I am now . . ." Next day she sent the cake round our house with a letter stuck to one of t' horse-shoes. Summut about breach of promise. I got me bike out and went to her place. She got right stroppy so I gave her a wing-winder across the bonce and that was that.'

'Ye've had a close squeak all right,' sighed the Badger.

'I 'ave an' all.'

'Make yer blood run cold to think of it.'

'Aye. Does an' all.'

'Whatcha goin' er do if she come after yer?'

'I'm not goin' down Thorold Street in t'daylight. I know that much.'

'You're right an' all.'

'I am.'

'She'll get yer else.'

'Aye. She can run like a bloody greyhound when the mood takes her.'

Having eaten the cake they started to sing:

> 'If her knickers are navy blue
> That's Peggy O'Neil
> If she lets you have a blow through
> That's Peggy O'Neil.'

The Badger joined in, sounding like twenty caged lions:

> 'She may charge a tanner
> She may charge a bob
> It all depends on the size of yer knob.'

No one could remember the rest – so they sang it all again.

By the time the last tier of the cake had been demolished the party had developed on the heroic scale. A few very blurred images come to mind, none of them in sharp focus but all warranted true. Buster, with a smile like Christmas morning, pouring everyone drinks from Paddy's bottle. All Sorts pushing his head through the serving hatch at the same moment as the shutter fell and trapped him. Barry passing the mess-deck and stopping with a stunned expression before hurrying away. Ken being sewn up into a net, complete with bottle. The Skipper's face as he appeared unexpectedly on the bridge and watched a wavy line of deckies descend the fo'c'sle starboard and appear again on the port, each bulging with bottles and cases of beer. Empties ejected like torpedoes from the port-holes. Wacker splayed out like a starfish (the party's only casualty) murmuring: 'Wake me when we reach the Humber, somebody.' Rubber Nose, fully clothed, trying to find his way out of the shower cubicle which was working full blast. The Badger doing the Cossack Dance – faultlessly – on the mess-deck table. More empties ejected from port-holes. Yorkie looking sullen. The return of Barry, still looking stunned. The Badger, once more, lifting Ken at the end of a shovel . . . Everyone lifting bottles, cans and glasses, endlessly, until the last drop had gone. Ken waking Wacker to tell him the Humber lightship was now astern.

It was – as far as anyone remembered – quite a party. The mess-deck smelt like a gin palace for days afterwards, and no one remembered to release All Sorts from the hatch shutter.

CHAPTER THIRTY-FOUR

The Sparks had spent most of the last few days monitoring the flow of information coming in over the receiver and radio telephone. Most of it concealed rather than revealed anything, and the information likely to be of most use was scrambled anyway, or transmitted in code. Nevertheless, it was worth listening in to the interminable conversations between other skippers, in the hope that between the two-edged pleasantries and deceptively friendly banter something might be leaked which would reveal who was turning for home and when. The Gaffers had wired *Arctic Fox* giving reports showing the state of the market back at G.Y., but it was the Skipper who had to weigh one set of facts against all others, and make a decision. Such contingencies as might arise had to be faced, not least the ever changing sea itself.

Mariners never trust the sea, particularly the North Sea. It is prone to sudden gales, mostly from the north-east, which in force and intensity equal anything the Atlantic has to offer, and many a market has been lost, and with it many thousands of pounds, when a following wind has veered round and become a head wind half way across the North Sea. On a previous trip *Arctic Fox* had herself arrived at the dock gates five minutes after they closed and missed her market; a gross of £10,000 became a gross of £3,280, which in terms of hard won cash was a bitter loss for the crew to bear. The loss was caused by a falling off in quality, resulting from the twelve hours' delay, and to heavy landings by foreign vessels which led to a glut of cod.

Most of the crew had accepted the circumstances which had made them trawlermen. There were protestations, outbursts of defiance, which took them ashore or to the oil rigs, but they missed the freedom and their hearts protested, too, and soon they were back at sea again. Ashore they were not aware of themselves in context. They often complained of feeling lonely. There was never any time to make compromises, and when they tried they failed. They misunderstood the suburban obligations they had tried so hard to attain. The code was too rigid, the rules too circumscribed, the uniformity too destructive. They simply gave it up and went back to sea. There was always the pub to come back to. Once ashore they crowded the familiar impermanent bars along Freeman Street and gazed out at a transient world which touched them briefly for a day or two – and then they shouldered their sea bags containing the only things that really belonged to them and put to sea again.

At twenty, ambitions were still retrievable – there was no feeling of lost opportunity. At thirty, failure could be exorcised with a bottle of rum. It is only at forty, when there are no excuses left and the essential prowess has already begun to fall away, that there comes for many fishermen a bitter acceptance of things as they are. As Buster says: 'Can't all be mates and skippers, can we?' And the embittered Yorkie: 'All I can 'ope for is a win on the Pools, or I've 'ad it,' and after a pause, 'It's the sea, she won't *let* me go'. And the Badger: 'It'll all be the same in the end, me old son, so why worry?'

Deckmen are all reluctant voyagers, and in answer to the question, 'Signing on next trip?' would reply, 'I'll see,' or 'Depends what I pick up this trip,' or simply, 'Don't know'. A third of *Arctic Fox's* crew would make the base compromise of signing on another ship, some would be *told* to sign off, and the rest would be back in *Arctic Fox*. Or would they . . . ?

'I'm giving it up 'cause my dad was lost out this way. That leaves just my mum and me.'

'. . . going into partnership with a bloke who runs an amusement arcade.'

'Me? I'm joining my sister – she's got a newspaper shop.'

'Sign back on this sand-scratcher – not likely!'

'Fishing's had it from me. I'm getting a shore job this winter.'

It was all so easy, after all. Beyond the level crossing at the end of Fish Dock road the old familiar dream was still waiting. The familiar impermanent bars along Freeman Street would still be open. The tinsel of the dance hall and the gay, predatory market. Permanent reminders of a longing so easily satisfied. One only had to sign off, and the reason was always there.

'Trawling's not a job, it's only an existence.'

'We earn money like men and spend it like fools.'

'It's no life for a man, and it's worse for the wife and bairns.'

'You have to make the break while you're still young, or else.'

'It's worse if you're born to it – your folks think you're afraid. I am sometimes.'

These hopes and criticisms could safely be expressed at sea, but if the same questions were asked ashore the answers would be different. After long silent intervals, followed by self-deprecating, self-deceiving gestures, the quick surrender would begin. The call of the sea would be echoed by the gulls and reflected in the brown waters of the Humber, and slowly men would disappear. The call had to be answered.

'We're closing with the land,' remarked Bill, glancing out through the clear vision panel on the bridge. 'If the wind holds we should see the coastline about an hour from now.'

Landfall appeared 57 minutes later. Through the morning haze the long low shore of Scotland broke in remote disorder where the rocks touched the sea. The sea, calm and impossibly blue, caressed the ship's rail with white fingers before falling back in powdered spray. Through binoculars one could see green fields rolling gently away from the white cliffs and farmhouses standing in friendly isolation in the fertile valleys.

'It's good to see land again,' said Bill.

CHAPTER THIRTY-FIVE

The bridge log clicked away the miles. Early risers pointed out the surf dancing at the foot of Flamborough Head. At noon the slender finger of Spurn Point fell astern. Debris tumbled in the wake, and the odour of fish compounded over four and a half centuries carried on the breeze.

Keeping station with the north shore of the Humber, *Arctic Fox* made her way up river between the channel buoys ready to wait at anchor. From the shore an Aldis flashed a signal.

'We've got the second berth.' The Sparks spoke over his shoulder to the Mate.

'Pity we've not got a market tide as well. Who's landing with us?'

'Only four for Tuesday.'

'If we had made Monday's market on a market tide with a low berth number we'd have cleared ten thousand quid. With our fish tally and twenty-two days to landing we might have made more.'

'We're still head of the market. Ken.'

'Aye, just. On my reckoning we'll make eight thousand; a bit more if we're lucky. No use chuntering about it I suppose. It's all luck in this game.'

The tide caught the bow as *Arctic Fox* lost way before casting anchor. With the clutch off the windlass, the cable followed the anchor into the sea. The Ensign broke on the pole and kicked fitfully in the wind. Above the low hum of the dynamo the brown water gurgled against the plates.

Arctic Fox's escort flew out to see her into her home port. These common denizens of Grimsby, sitting sentinel on the covered bays of the fish market and on buildings fronting the jetties, are always on the watch for returning trawlers and, unlike their Arctic cousins, the Grimsby gulls will settle on a ship. They are known in fishing ports as 'Retired Skippers'.

They gathered round *Arctic Fox* in noisy hoards and welcomed her with wild cries, and then took up station until the ship was dressed overall in white feathers and flesh pink feet. They could tell a fishing boat from those that were of no interest to them, and enjoyed standing on the forepeak as though on watch. Upwards of forty stood to attention on the whaleback and stared accusingly at the bridge. As the wind veered to about two points off the bow they turned – all at the same moment – to face the shore. When it veered back, they turned towards the bridge again, still simulating hunger. The gulls provide (and the fact does not pass unnoticed) the first physical link with home.

'When the Grimsby Mollies come out to see you through the pits it's nearly all over – you can say you're home.'

Other links with home would have already been made. The Docks V.H.F. radio would be keeping tidal watch and the first visual sighting of the battered trawler noted down. The private telegram service would be reassuring next of kin: 'You will be pleased to know that the steam trawler *Arctic Fox* has wired and expects to dock Grimsby on Monday the 23rd January 1967 – Happy Landings!' The familiar tide tables would be consulted and wives, children and girl friends assemble self-consciously along the edge of the covered fish market to await the ship.

Others would leave front doors unlocked or keys under milk bottles with the occasional cryptic message, 'Supper's in oven' or 'Don't knock – my husband's back on days'.

In twenty-one days *Arctic Fox* had steamed a distance of 3,421 nautical miles – equal to the round trip from Grimsby to New York. In 80 hauls she had caught 126 ton of fish – enough to provide a meal for 280,000 families. Price per stone, at ship's side, heads on, would be in the region of: 12s. for Shelf Cod. Large Haddock 14s. Plaice 20s. Coalfish 6s. Catfish 7s. 6d. Repairs would keep her in dry dock for six weeks at a loss of £400 a day for the owners.

If she realised a gross of £10,000 she would have made an above average trip. From this gross the Skipper would be paid £54 for every £1,000, bringing his percentage earnings to £540 for 21 days' work. In contrast the deckies would receive £6 12s. 6d. in every £1,000 and gross £66 5s. 0d., which would be around £50 after tax deductions. From the owners' share, two-thirds of the gross value of the catch would be absorbed in fuel oil and payment to the crew, with marine insurance as an extra. Tug charges (£18), changing jetties (£20), moving in dock (£11), use of tug hawser (£2), compass adjusters (£27) and harbour dues would also have to be met from the balance, along with incidentals such as the cost of a nightwatchman whilst in port and the varied items of ships' chandlery.

The damage *Arctic Fox* had sustained could give rise to arbitration and result in further expense for the Gaffers. If the damage was considered unavoidable the cost of repair would fall upon the insurers in proportion to their shares of the particular interests affected. If intentional, (as by inviting hazard resulting in the cutting away of masts, loss of lifeboats), the insurers' obligations would probably depend on subsequent enquiry centreing on 'losses incidental to marine adventure'. The owners would have to meet every one of these expenses and charges, even if the ship made *nothing*. The only exception would be the crew's percentage, which would also amount to nothing. Such expenses would not include replacement nets and trawl gear, which in *Arctic Fox's* case would be heavy.

Considered in the light of the cost involved, the business of catching the nation's fish remains as much a gamble for the Gaffers as it does for those actively involved. It also explains – even if it does not justify – the razor-edge existence of the less successful skippers, and the ruthless determination of the remainder.

CHAPTER THIRTY-SIX

This had been a hard voyage, but not without precedent in January above the 74th parallel. The crew viewed it with their customary detachment, and some had presumably forgotten it altogether. For them it belonged to yesterday. The day after tomorrow they would see it all again.

Arctic Fox weighed anchor and got slowly under way – rolling gently as she headed up river between the lights of the channel buoys. Slowly, from light to light, sweeping wide round the last bend of the estuary, she reached for home. Suddenly, the lights of Grimsby, and minutes later the red brick clock tower black against the afternoon sky.

The Sparks called from the chart room.

'Just coming on the bearing now, Skipper.'

The Skipper turned to Paddy.

'Take her in, but not too fast. The Dock Master's complaining about damage again.'

With practised ease the ship completed a wide sheer.

The austere silhouette of Grimsby to which the irregular pattern of masts gave effective counterpoint looked old and dirty. The rebuilt No. 1 Fish Dock looked smaller than it really was, and less substantial. Fish was being smoked between No. 2 Fish Dock and Cleethorpes Road. There was something special about Grimsby on a home tide – something in the spiced wind blowing from the land quickened the pulse. The smell of the sea evoked tarred rigging in the days of sail.

The Signal Mast between the locks on Fish Dock Island showed her red light seaward. *Arctic Fox* continued slowly under way. Within minutes the Signal Post on the east corner of the Fish Dock Cutting flashed green over white. *Arctic Fox* had permission to enter harbour. The Skipper acknowledged, and the shore light was extinguished. A small ship with her bow overhanging a buoy swung on the tide, and its stern light missed *Arctic Fox's* quarter rail by inches. The Mate, who had just clumped his way up the bridge ladder, flung himself across the bridge and crashed down the window on the port wing.

'Keep that fucking heap of rust clear, will you!'

The small ship continued to swing out. The Mate depressed the Tannoy switch and turned the volume up.

'Bloody foreigners,' he muttered. 'LISTEN, YOU FOREIGN PEASANTS! GET THAT PILE OF SHIT OUT OF THE WAY! CLEAR OFF – GIVE US SEAWAY OR I'LL PUNCH DAYLIGHT THROUGH YOU!'

Looking pleased, he kept up his tirade until quite suddenly he recognised the occupant of the other ship's bridge.

'Hello, Chukker.' (Face all smiles.) 'See you on the pontoon later?'

Pushing up the window he turned to Paddy at the wheel and remarked pleasantly: 'That was Chukker ... friend of mine ... didn't recognise him at first.'

Coming up before the lock, *Arctic Fox* lost way and stopped before the gates. Atop the mast of the lock gates the signal still showed red. The eight-knot tide had not made sufficiently. The ship's cable thundered out over the monkey and the anchor crashed into the sea. She lay silent and still, with the crescent of shore lights gleaming fitfully through the open scupper ports. The signal went out, and moments later the green came on. The gates were already open.

Arctic Fox recovered her anchor and swung quartering to the sea. Colin descended to the chain locker to watch the lay of the cable. It was a filthy job, and somehow he always fell for it.

The ship was now free to pass through the lock, using the

West Pier entrance. With fenders over, *Arctic Fox* edged her way through the pit into the narrow pool. At 'Slow Ahead' she worked her way up the dock between the moored ships – past the Brenda Fisher who hooted a greeting. There was no formality other than this. Just a bluff greeting. There was no call for 'Hands to station for entering Port'. No Bosun's call. Just a few calm orders as the Ensign flickered on the staff. The Navy always overdid things.

The swing bridge showed amber. The way was clear to No. 1 Fish Dock, where she would pass through the 60 ft. wide entrance into No. 2 Fish Dock and tie up alongside the covered Fish Market hard by Chapman Jetty.

Fifteen members of *Arctic Fox's* crew stood along the rail. On the whaleback the Badger in his shore suit with a tie like the outside of a seed packet held a heaving line. *Arctic Fox* eased in, turning her bow to the landing stage. She came up slowly, stemming the tide, maintaining just enough revolutions to hold her position. Her bows lay less than a foot from land. Easing gently, she came alongside her berth on helm and engines. With the tide on the make, she ground along the wall and stopped. Lines snaked out and were secured to bollards ashore. The handle of the telegraph went down and the signal was acknowledged by the engine room.

'Finished with engines.'

In the port the early winter dusk had claimed the day. Somewhere a radio was playing. A small wave curled against the stem of *Arctic Fox* and sent ripples across the water. The dynamo whined to a stop and the ship merged into the background as her deck lights faded out. The rudder and wheel were put back amidships and all was suddenly still.

It remains to be recorded that:

'*Arctic Fox* was secured at her Port of Registry on Tuesday the 24th day of January 1967 at 16 minutes past 4 on the P.M. tide; inward bound from distant waters with a cargo of wet fish.

. . . sustained damage from meeting natural hazards in impaired visibility. Listing starboard and down by the head resulting (in part) from collision with ice in Arctic waters. Failure of navigational aids in partially charted regions impaired handling. Ship obeyed helm with difficulty but was otherwise under effective command.

Made port unaided and docked without assistance. All Port Entry procedures observed and Ensign worn from staff at stern.

Manifest Declaration endorsed by H.M. Customs after berthing. All bonded stores secured and sealed.

Trawler sustained no loss from amongst her crew and returned with all hands aboard as listed in Ship's Articles.'

May this always be so.

GLOSSARY

BAG: The amount of fish enclosed in the cod end, once secured by the halving becket. Capacity = 2 tons.

BANJO: Single slice of bread topped with meat or cheese.

BECKET: Manilla rope made endless, with loop spliced in at each end.

BELLY: Triangular section of net, forming part of underside of trawl.

BIKE: Ship's wheel.

BITT: Steel section secured to deck, used to turn warps or as cable guide.

BOBBIN: Hollow steel ball 24 in., 26 in. or 28 in. diameter reeved through ground wire on lower part of trawl.

BOLSH: Manilla rope.

BRIDLE: Connects warp wire to doors by means of swivel.

BULKHEAD: Vertical partition dividing up compartments of ship.

BUSTERS: Bread rolls.

CABLE LENGTH: 100 fathoms (600 ft.).

CLEAT: Iron projecting piece for fastening ropes and preventing them from slipping.

COD END: End section of Granton trawl attached to belly.

COD LINE: Nylon rope threaded through the Cod End and tied so as to facilitate quick release of fish.

COWHIDES: Tied to underside of Cod End to protect same from abrasion and wear caused by dragging along sea bed.

DAN LENO: Iron half sphere (one of two) connecting trawl end of bridle to edge of trawl mouth.

DONKEY: Power for water hose.

DOORS: Of timber and wood construction with heavy iron runner shoe along lower edge. Their function is to divert the warps at an angle favourable to the continued spread of the trawl.

FATHOM: Six feet.

FISH-SHOP: Large shoal of fish.

FREEBOARD: Distance of ship's side from floatation to deck level.

GALLOWS: Steel arches used to secure doors and raise and lower them by means of pulley block and sheave through which warp travels.

GASH: Extra food or dram, or extra time below in bunk.

GOBBLING IRONS: Knives and forks.

GILSON: Wire rope passed through a system of pulleys and designed to lift end of trawl inboard by means of winding free end round revolving winch barrel.

GRIMMIES': Fishermen from Grimsby.

GROWLER: Small iceberg.

GUNWHALE: Upper edge of ship's side.

G.Y. or GY: Grimsby.

HALVING BECKET: Endless wire rope, loop spliced in at each

end. Used to encircle Cod End thus preventing the catch run-ning back into the belly of trawl.

HANGING ON THE SLACK: Pretending to exert pressure where none is needed.

HAULING: Bringing gear and catch back inboard at end of tow.

HOVEL: Any vessel abandoned on the high seas.

JOCKEYS' WHIPS: Chips.

JOSSERS: Small cod fish.

JUMBOS: Large haddocks.

KIT (of fish): 10 stone or 140 pounds.

KNOT: A speed of 1 nautical mile per hour.

LEGLESS: Drunk.

LUMPERS: Landing labourers.

MESSENGER: Acid grade, plough steel, wire rope used in con-junction with hook to bring both warps together so that these can be secured in towing block.

MOLLIES: Gulls.

MUSICAL FRUIT: Peas.

NAUTICAL MILE: Equal to 1.151 statute (land) miles.*

PLONK: Port or sherry.

POTS: Tea cups.

POUNDS: Pens on foredeck where catch is released and later gutted.

RICKSHAW PETROL: Rice.

SCUPPER: Shuttered opening in ship's side above water line. Allows water to run from deck back into sea.

SHACKLES: Meat, potatoes, carrots, in pot.

SHEAVE: Free running grooved pulley wheel, mounted in block.

SHOOTING: Putting gear outboard at the commencement of towing.

SKED: Radio report on fishing over a given area.

SPARKS: Radio Officer.

SPRAGS: Cod fish.

SURGE: Allowing wire or rope cables to ride free of tension on winch barrel.

TOWING BLOCK: Encloses both warps and holds them secure so that ship is free to manoeuvre whilst towing.

WARP: Steel wire cable 30mm. in diameter extending from Port and Starboard winch drums, round bollards and shackled to doors. Providing the only means by which the complete trawl is towed astern of the vessel.

WHERE AWAY?: A question passed to a look-out by anyone want-ing precise information about the bearing of an object.

WHIFFLE: Avoiding duty.

'YORKIE': Hull fisherman.

*The sea mile is divided into 10 cables, a cable being usually accepted as 600 ft. When used in navigation to measure distances it is defined as the length of a minute of latitude (i.e. one sixtieth of a degree).

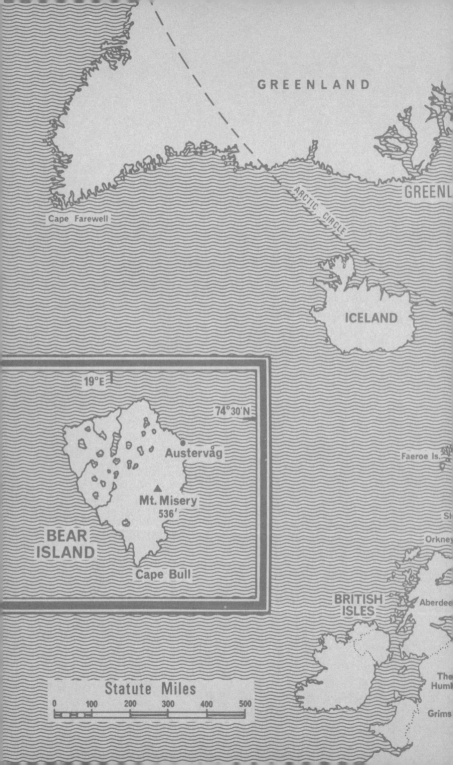